A Treasury of
The World's Finest Folk Song

A TREASURY
OF THE WORLD'S
FINEST FOLK SONG

Collected and arranged by

LEONHARD DEUTSCH

With explanatory text by

CLAUDE SIMPSON

Lyrics versified by Willard Trask
Guitar chords by Michael Jaffee
Illustrations by Emery I. Gondor

CROWN PUBLISHERS, INC., NEW YORK

The publisher gratefully acknowledges the following, who have gener-
ously contributed their time and expertise to edit and/or transliterate
verses in the original languages: Miquel Barceló, Paul Blumenthal,
Catherine S. Carr, Platon Elias, Maria A. Gargotta, Ihor Hubarshevsky,
Carl Allen Kinbar, Rado L. Lencek, Beatrice M. Nosco, Gratiana Piz-
zaro, Anicetas Simutis, Éva Uhljár, and Stephen Werner. Ruth Ronall
rates special attention for her kind cooperation, which made this edition
at all possible.

Foreword

When I was a youth, my native Vienna was the capital of an Empire which embraced a population of 56,000,000 persons in eleven nations. The furthest corners of the Monarchy supplied Vienna with a steady stream of Czechs, Slovaks, Croations, Hungarians, Slovenians—peoples of every class and of almost every nationality. Vienna was a truly cosmopolitan city, but it put its own stamp on the immigrants. They gave up their original culture, sometimes even abandoned their own language. Yet they kept their songs, and singing them, gave the city an incomparably rich folk literature. Like many other children of Old Vienna, I absorbed these folksongs naturally and sang them as a matter of course. But when I grew older and took up formal music study, I forsook my childhood songs. Compared with the music of the great masters, folk music seemed to me primitive and inferior.

Later, however, I revised my opinion radically. I had an opportunity to hear folksongs in their natural rural setting. I discovered that in remote villages, far from the rarefied atmosphere of the concert hall, the country folk sang spontaneously, yet as from some inner necessity. I realized the deep emotion, the clear freshness, the inevitability of folk music when it plays a vigorous part in the lives of simple people. I was even more strongly impressed by the power of artless music while I was in the Austro-Hungarian army of the First World War. There the songs appeared in the full variety of their national color, sung by soldiers, prisoners, nomadic Gypsies and other followers of the army. They all sang their songs incessantly, singly or in groups. It was their only solace in hours of boredom, misery or horror.

My experiences convinced me that my old "academic" prejudices were ill-founded. There was, I discovered, a relationship between the genius of the great composers and the genius of the unlettered folk. Highly musical peoples such as Poles, Italians, Czechs, Slovakians and Hungarians had likewise a fine body of folk music. Indeed, these songs helped to keep the formal musical tradition alive. I have no doubt that the musical soil of Old Vienna was richly fertilized by the folksongs imported from the various nations of the Hapsburg Monarchy. And what is true of a city is even more significant of village and countryside where music is an integral part of everyone's life, and there is no class line.

My new view of folksong inspired me with the idea of reforming music instruction so that even the most elementary pupil should feel that same intimacy with music. If the simple man of the folk possessed his music as though it were a natural right, I was sure that with the help of folksong I could transplant some of this simple, unconscious sense of ownership to students of music everywhere.

It took many years to work out this idea in detail. The volumes I published were received with a warmth that surpassed my expectations. Since that time many other music teachers have adopted similar methods; in other countries, including America, the theory has become almost a commonplace in musical instruction.

When I began my researches, I saw that I should have to make a thorough study of the folksong literature of all nations. I soon found myself in a new realm of music whose richness and variety I had not even suspected. The folksongs I had previously known were but an infinitesimal fraction of what had been collected since the beginning of the nineteenth century. And I discovered that, as in all art, excellence and mediocrity were to be encountered and discriminated. By patient searching I proved to myself that there were folksongs which could be judged by the most exacting musical standards of classicism and romanticism, and that the jewels of folk literature were worthy to shine in any crown.

"Infinite riches in a little room!" Christopher Marlowe's phrase exactly defines the peculiar excellence of the best folksong. For it is *intensity* which distinguishes folksong from artsong. In beauty of form, profundity and maturity of expression, power and originality of invention, the masterpieces of the composer and of the folk are comparable. But only the folksong achieves a maximum of intensity, distilled, as it were, through generations of oral circulation during which the volatile elements have evaporated.

But folksongs of this high quality are rare. Moreover, they are inaccessible, and the average musician has neither gone among the people to seize them alive, nor searched the voluminous archives of popular music. This book, so far as I know, is the first international collection of folksongs assembled on strictly musical and artistic principles. I have sought to include only what is musically first-rate; I have not tried to exhibit "characteristic" popular or national songs, nor have I made any effort to run the gamut of subject-matter or musical style of any folk group. To do so would have been to dup-

licate the work of Reimann, Bantock, Botsford, Möller and others. My simple criterion is not folkloristic, not chauvinistic—it is purely musical.

In this book I have tried to rescue this most living and dynamic form of song from the libraries and archives in which much of it lies buried. I have presented the songs as an entity, a total spectrum made up of colors each pure and splendid in its own right.

In my arrangements I have, of course, retained the original form of the tunes, and have nowhere tried to "improve" rhythm or melodic line. For practical purposes I have usually included the melodies in the piano accompaniments, but they may be left out at will. I have made the accompaniments as unpretentious as possible, feeling that they should fill out the harmonic patterns implicit in the melody, but that they should be as simple as is consistent with good musicianship.

The task of providing English lyrics for many of the songs in this collection has been a difficult one, for it has involved the maintenance of the true rhythm and rhymes of the original as they are determined by the music. This was especially true in the translation from Eastern-European languages which differ radically from all the Western languages, and from English. The lack of up-beats, the frequent syncopations, the accumulation of long syllables and other peculiarities of these Eastern languages added to the difficulty. Beyond that, the songs in this collection have been selected purely for their musical value and, because they are folksongs, without consideration of the text. Thus Mr. Willard Trask was often forced to deal not only with the technical difficulties of alien poetry, but also with texts not especially worthy of transcription because of their slight poetic substance. The translator has endeavored to make each song singable as well as intelligible and has therefore sometimes had to correct, retouch, abbreviate and interpret the meaning of the available original. All these expedients, however, were used only when they were necessary. The original meaning of the poems has been preserved as literally as possible and nowhere has the meaning been changed radically.

I hope that this book will emphasize the rightful place of folksong in serious vocal literature. If it succeeds it may, in turn, help to reawaken a feeling for melody which our generation seems to have forgotten.

LEONHARD DEUTSCH

GUITAR CHORDS

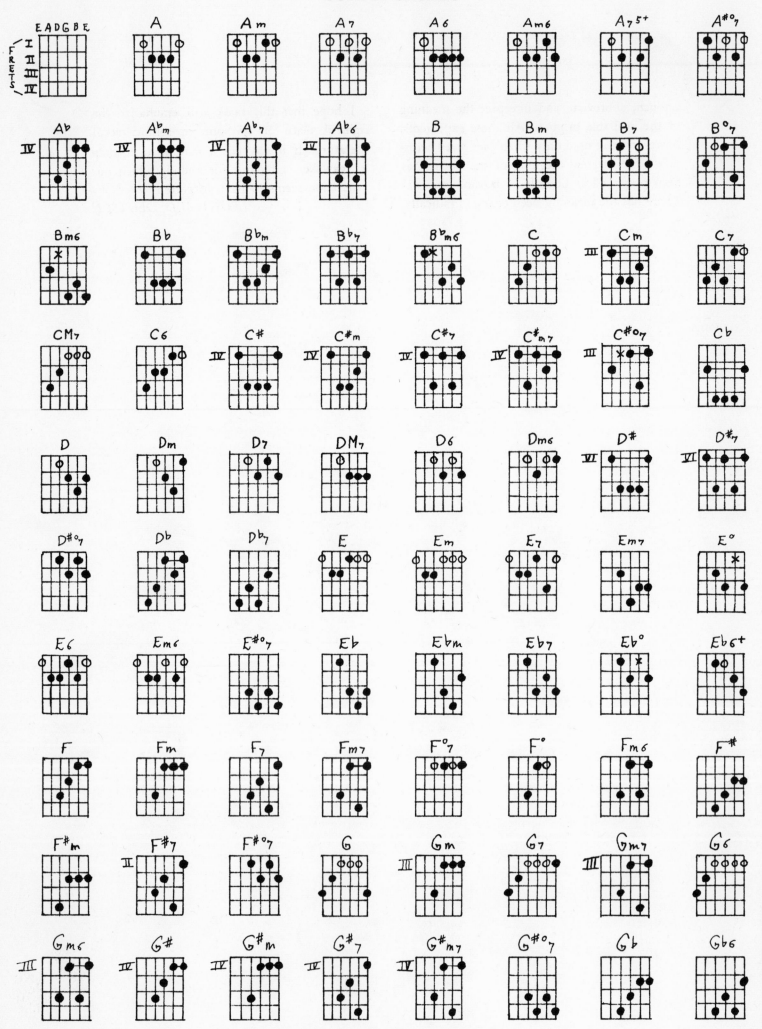

Preface

IN THIS NEW EDITION of Leonhard Deutsch's *A Treasury of the World's Finest Folk Song,* the publishers have sought to make the songs readily accessible to guitarists as well as to pianists. All the chords necessary to play the songs are diagramed on the accompanying chord chart. The chords indicated in the chart can be played by either the pick or finger-style guitarist, and have been made as simple as possible.

As a rule, the guitar chords were chosen to correspond to the harmonic progressions in the piano accompaniments. Where this procedure proved unfeasible, either a close equivalent was selected or a new harmonization was substituted for the original. In the case of such alterations, the chord substitution was chosen to conform as closely as possible to the harmonic implications of the melodic line. In a few introductions where the piano versions are particularly complex (such as the introduction to the Italian song "When I Raise My Eyes," page 129), only the principal chords are indicated as a guide to establishing the key. Where unusually complex chords have been retained, enharmonic equivalents are sometimes employed to enable the

player to use a chord he probably already knows (for example, the seventh chords substituted for augmented-sixth chords in the French song "Springtime Is Here," page 103).

All the chords on the chart are diagramed in root position, with the exception of a few diminished-seventh chords. In the few cases where inversions may be desirable, the experienced player can provide his own substitutions. Bar chords are always indicated with a minimum of notes to the bar; again, it is left to the more advanced player to supply additional notes at his discretion.

In any folk-song accompaniment, several harmonizations are usually possible. The ones given here are by no means the only solutions to be found, and part of the enjoyment of performing a folk song lies in the spontaneous invention of both singer and player. Many of the melodies will suggest a particular strum, arpeggio, or rhythmic pattern, as well as a variety of harmonizations. The guitarist is therefore encouraged to let his musical intuition serve as a guide, and in so doing he will enrich his enjoyment of the many wonderful songs to be found in this book.

M. J.

Contents

NOTE ON THE PRONUNCIATION
OF SLAVIC SOUNDS

Some sounds in Slavic languages, the texts of which appear in the transliteration from their Cyrillic alphabets (that is, for Russian, Ukrainian, Bulgarian, and Serbian), may differ from English sounds. The following list of letters used in our texts represents all the major deviations, and gives their approximation:

a   as in English *father*
e   as in b*e*t
ë   as in *ya*wn
i   as in b*ee*t
o   as in l*aw*
u   as in b*oo*t
y   as in t*i*ll

c   as in ha*ts,* or German *z*ehn
č   as in *ch*eap
š   as in *sh*eep
ž   as in plea*s*ure
ć   as in *tu*ne
dj   as in *J*im
kh   as in Ba*ch*
j   as in *y*es
r   is trilled with the tip of the tongue
’   soft sign, symbolizes a palatal pronunciation of the preceding consonant; see Note.

NOTE: In the Russian language all but three consonants (š, ž, c) are palatalized (that is, pronounced as if followed by a *y*) whenever they are followed by an *i*, *e*, or *j* letter, or by the soft sign.

Also, in Russian, an initial *e* is pronounced as *ye*.

INTRODUCTION

FOR CENTURIES a precious badge of identity for people everywhere has been the stock of folkways they have subconsciously absorbed and passed on from one generation to another. Our immediate interest is in the body of song preserved over a sizable expanse of geography and time, and fulfilling an organic role in voicing the fantasies and realities which make for ethnic or social unity. Traditional songs of the seasons, of religious and secular festivals, of marriages and funerals, of occupations, of happy and tragic love, are all commonplace inheritances of the folk.

There are, generally speaking, three kinds of song which the people may sing, and it is well to make a distinction among them. The first is the art song, written by a skilled musician employing all his technical knowledge and artistic ability. It lives only by being sung, of course, but it circulates in published form and is usually intended for trained singers. The work of Schubert, Hugo Wolf, or Thomas Campion comes to mind as examples of the art song. A second variety may be called the popular song. It too is written by individuals more or less skilled in their craft, but its circulation is not limited to trained singers. For a time it may be on every lip, and it may even circulate independently of the printed page. Our American "popular music" is a good, though not the only, example of this genre. The topical song or broadside is another variety of popular song, often used for political or religious propaganda, a powerful weapon in recurrent moments of crisis.

The third type of song, and the one with which we are particularly concerned here, is the folk song. It too must have had an original author, although only in rare cases is his identity known; its circulation is oral, without the benefit of the printed page, and its traditional character is established by its currency among generation after generation of the folk. Mere anonymity of authorship is not crucial in creating a folk song, but its oral transmission over a substantial period of time is decisive, and so also is its spontaneous use by the folk (which ordinarily rules out patriotic "national" songs from this category).

It was once fashionable to say that the ballad and the lyric originated through communal composition. That theory is now generally discounted, but it is illuminating and valid in one respect. The song which is transmitted only by oral means is fluid; there is no fixed text, no rigidly defined tune. In this sense the folk song is constantly being refashioned as it passes from one singer to another, and in essence we have finally a species of cooperative or communal authorship. Changes due to lapse of memory, or misunderstanding, or a momentary creative urge are constantly altering the original form of the song. We are not surprised to see the Scotch ballad of "Lord Randall" turning up in Virginia with a protagonist named Jimmy Randall, or being sung in a foreshortened version as a cradle song in northern England, where the chief character has become a "Wee Croodin' Doo."

Such examples as these emphasize another important aspect of traditional song—its acceptance by the folk over a considerable area. The Scotch border ballads do not respect political boundaries, but have crossed over to England and so to the United States. Many folk songs of the Wends derive from German originals, just as the folk traditions of the Ukraine and southern Poland tend to merge, and songs of northern Italy are patent migrations from the Provence. Ordinarily it is next to impossible to assign priority to one of several versions of a folk song. And as a corollary, there is no one text which can be considered original or standard, from which others may be said to deviate. Even when we can sometimes detect the relative antiquity of several specimens before us, we must recognize the vitality and authority of each, although we may judge one version "better" than another.

It is perhaps dangerous to speak of the folk song in

aesthetic terms. For to do so is to judge by formalized and academic standards a genre which has survived amid critical judgments of an entirely different sort. Yet it is inevitable that this form of popular expression be considered by musical and literary scholars, and that their opinions have a perceptible influence upon all of us. Thus we find the texts of ballads and folk songs praised for their conciseness of expression, their fine naïveté, their eloquent use of nature metaphors and similes. Or we find the music judged according to its variety and inventiveness, its classical or romantic form. Musical folklorists value the folk song according to the accuracy of the transcription, irrespective of its aesthetic qualities. The moralists, who have frequently wandered in, judge largely on the basis of coarseness—absent, present or implied. It is impossible to escape entirely some of the assumptions I have mentioned, yet I cannot help feeling that most of these criteria, while interesting and fruitful, are beside the point. One must, I think, meet the folk song on its own terms.

Someone has evolved the theory, and it is comfortably held by many romanticists, that an immutable law of progress unconsciously but surely guides the folk song. According to this belief, the longer a folk song lives the "purer" it becomes, as the unerring instinct of the folk purges text and music of all dross. A moment's thought will suggest that such a theory runs counter to human nature. And a study of the variants of a few songs will make it clear that chance, not any idealistic aim, governs the changes that take place. From any aesthetic point of view, if we may resort to value judgments for a moment, the alterations are as likely to be blemishes as improvements, and examples could be cited at length. It is evident that this "purification" theory is based on wishful thinking and not on any inspection of the evidence.

Another heresy worth comment concerns the naïveté and artlessness of the folk song, to which I have already alluded. This notion arises almost solely among persons whose interest is limited to the words of the folk song. To be sure, historical considerations confirm them when they find in the texts evidences of a primitive homogeneous society or hints of pagan superstition. Furthermore, there is no denying that the traditional love poetry of some nations is often banal and jejune. Here the bowdlerizing of texts leaves an unduly nice idea of social mores in an otherwise non-puritan society. But on the whole we may grant that artlessness and naïveté are frequently present in the song *texts*.

In the *music* the situation may be quite otherwise. The Finns and the Basques are fond of 5/4 time; the Bulgarians use even more complex measures—7/8, 9/16, 13/16 and the like, always carefully dividing them into two equal parts. The improvisational chants of the Yugoslavian *guslari* and the Spanish *flamenco* singers abound in subtle but florid ornament, and microtones are precisely employed. We may agree with the Hungarian musicologist Béla Bartók that, historically, folk song has evolved from irregular assymetrical elements toward a noticeable architectural structure. But despite the lack of form, in the classical sense, many of the oldest extant songs must impress us with their complexity. It is as a result of this very fact that modern researchers feel the need of electronically recording this "primitive" music, that they may be sure of capturing the nuances which might otherwise be lost. And the further we study the scrupulously transcribed airs, the more suspicious we are that an artificial regularity—a dubious simplification, if you will—has been imposed on thousands of tunes transcribed in the eighteenth and nineteenth centuries.

Nevertheless, folk art has flourished most actively in districts untouched by modern civilization. That is understandable, since traditional song is primarily a rural and village genre. As long as this culture exists unmolested it flourishes. But once urban fashions begin to compete with rural manners, the countryman becomes self-conscious. He does not change his ways, but his children do. It is a well-known fact that the cheap newspaper, radio, television, and the phonograph record have within the past generation brought Main Street into even the most inaccessible clearing. In the Southern hill country of America the fiddle tunes and play-party games and "ballats" are frowned on by the young people who look longingly at the city and are embarrassed that their native music seems old-fashioned beside the latest product of the commercial songsmiths. This same thing has been happening, with varying momentum, on every continent. This may be only a temporary phase in the history of folk music, but it is critical.

Fortunately for the world at large, the collection of traditional and popular music and poetry began early enough to rescue a good part of it from oblivion. Bishop Thomas Percy's publication of the *Reliques of Ancient English Poetry* in 1765 started the movement. Herder took it up ambitiously in Germany, and Trutovsky and Prach in Russia; Ritson in the British Isles soon afterward began to make systematic collections of airs. As the wave of nationalism swept over Europe in the Napoleonic years, country after country saw individuals and societies gather up the folk tales, proverbs, the narrative and lyric poetry, the music of peasant song and dance. Although editorial methods in the nineteenth century were less scrupulous than they might have been, some very fine collections were made, notably of Wendish and Serbian folk song and the ballads of England and Scandinavia. By the beginning of the present century, folklore expeditions into the out-of-the-way districts carried recording equipment and filled the archives of a dozen nations with thousands of cylinders, disks, and tapes which have been transcribed and gradually published. Béla Bartók and Zoltán Kodály were pioneers in this technique in central Europe and recorded a remarkable number of songs and dance tunes. A distinguished piece of field work in Yugoslavia was done in 1934–35 by the late Professor Milman Parry of Harvard, who recorded 300 double-sided disks of "women's songs" and 2,200 of epic poems, including two as long as the Odyssey, and many others some thousands of lines long. In America the Folksong Archive of the Library of Congress continues to add to its vast collection begun a generation ago by John A. and Alan Lomax. Had present-day techniques been available a century ago, it goes without saying that we should have a far more voluminous and accurate record of what our forefathers sang.

A striking folk song revival has taken place in America and Western Europe since World War II, and despite its dilution by modern imitations, parodies, and topical pieces, broad public acquaintance with traditional song has spread to the four corners of the earth.

A few words remain to be said about the salient characteristics of the folk song in various parts of Europe. A line drawn from Denmark to the Adriatic Sea roughly divides East from West. In densely populated Western Europe, civilization is of long standing, and its penetration into rural areas has left various racial groups with less individuality than in the eastern half of the continent. The traditions of art music have been so firmly established that popular music has influenced, and even displaced, older folk songs and dances. In the agricultural East, city and country have been more decisively separated, with the consequent preservation of provincial idioms. In the Southeast, the long presence of the Turk has left its traces in the exotic Byzantine scales and embellishments, and the primitive pentatonic scales have been retained here long after they have disappeared in more accessible regions. From North to South some general differences may also be observed. The quiet and serious Scandinavian spirit is oftenest expressed in minor tonalities, but the mood brightens as one moves southward across the continent. Spain and Italy by contrast offer the utmost in sensual, passionate, vivacious melody. Major keys are the rule, and even the airs in minor ordinarily reflect insouciance and gaiety.

If love lyrics seem to predominate, there is nonetheless the greatest imaginable variety in the subject matter of folk song. As I frequently point out in the commentaries which follow, the rituals of marriage and death, the annual and seasonal festivals, all have their conventional song, which in some countries is exceedingly elaborate. And songs of satire and jest, tavern pieces, work songs and extemporized lyrics vie with the ubiquitous dancing songs of all nations. But however great the diversity of text and music, through all the genuine folk song shines undimmed the sincere spirit of the folk in all its moods, from despair to ecstasy.

A Slovakian peasant woman in conversation with a friend was once heard to remark, "I am so worried about my son Janko. He never sings." Behind such a slight remark lies a conception of life at once wonderful and strange to many Americans who have become accustomed to think of music as a purely professional commodity. Books tell us how to listen to music, and we have an active musical life, to be sure: we fill hundreds of concert halls, we buy millions of records, we are bathed in a sea of sound from dawn to midnight. But we are usually listening to someone else's music. If we are exacting in our standards, so much to the good. Yet what a distance separates the music business of the world's capitals from the spontaneous, almost involuntary song of the folk. With them, participation is everything, the audience incidental or nonexistent. Women in the Hebrides Islands constantly lighten their labors by singing as they weave or spin or milk or drive the sheep; the Latvian peasant year is a crowded almanac with a *daina* for every sort of seasonal festival and daily occupation; the Slovakian mother, as she despaired of her son, was doubtless thinking of the energetic dancing songs that all the Slavic peoples can take for granted as part of their recreation.

If the sophisticated world has cut itself off from its own music-making, the reasons are too clear to need repeating. It is difficult to assume that without worldwide calamity we shall return to a homestead civilization where life will be simple and we shall all be peasants together. But without wishing to imitate the Yugoslavian shepherd or the Hebridean weavers, we may well look into the treasuries of the folk music that have made Europe a singing continent. There are plentiful signs that we are no longer condescending toward the rich folk music of our own country, that we have discovered an unsuspected reality in our own past. The world of tomorrow will call for an even greater understanding of peoples who are as yet strange to us. Here is a chance to see them with as little distortion as distance and linguistic barriers will permit.

CLAUDE SIMPSON

Scandinavian

OUTSIDE THE BRITISH, perhaps no European peoples have been so characteristically nautical as have the Scandinavians. For many centuries they have been wedded to fishing, commerce and colonization. In the early centuries of the Christian era the Norsemen were among the most vigorous and venturesome peoples of the Continent. These aggressive and foolhardy Vikings harried the coast of France and England, and returned to colonize. Later, in the eighth century, a new race of Danes conquered the northern half of England and exacted tribute from the Anglo-Saxons. The famous Leif Ericson roamed so widely that in the year 1000 he was exploring American shores. With the Norman Conquest the hold on the British Isles relaxed, and for almost a thousand years the Scandinavian countries have been substantially what they are today. During this millennium Norway was ruled by the Danes for several hundred years and by the Swedes for a century; Sweden held domain over Finland and even over a stretch of the southern Baltic coast for a time. But by and large the Scandinavian nations have enjoyed a more stable geography and a more homogeneous growth than most other European nations.

The culture of modern Scandinavia, from which our folksongs come, is a product of the past two centuries, but it has its roots deep in the past. The heroic and mythological poems of the Elder Edda are part of the rich Old Norse (or Old Icelandic) literature which dates from the early middle ages. By 1200, fashions in poetry were changing, and the narrative folksong which we know as the ballad had begun to spread through the Scandinavian countries and thence to Britain and the rest of Europe. A large number of these medieval ballads have come down to us. Svend Gruntvig and Axel Olrik over a period of more than half a century (1853-1920) published a monumental collection of the Danish ballads with their innumerable variants, and the music to many of these *kjaempeviser* has also been recovered and published. In the isolated Faeroe Islands the old heroic narrative songs have been especially well preserved. Epic songs incorporating parts of the Nibelung story are still sung, along with more recent ballads, and we know them to have been unaccompanied singing dances chanted by a leader and his followers. Because of its antiquity, but also because of its high artistic quality, the Scandinavian epic and ballad material is of great importance.

In more recent times music has continued to be a precious commodity. King Christian IV of Denmark (1588-1648), for example, brought over the famous English musician and composer John Dowland to be court lutenist, and went to great lengths to establish a musically brilliant court. Nobility and gentry continued the wholesale importation of culture until recently. For the people as a whole, however, the folksong and folk dance have been dominant forms of popular expression, and upon these folk idioms have been based the work of most of the modern composers, including Grieg.

The Scandinavian folksong of the last two centuries comprises virtually a commonly shared body of themes and even texts. Making allowance for natural variants, scholars have long pointed to the widespread diffusion of such folksongs. But they are usually referring to texts. There may be some basis for the theory that words, ideas, themes travel with less impedance than does the supposedly universal language of music. At any rate, individuality among the Scandinavian nations is to be found in music to a greater extent than in texts. But even so, there is an essential kinship of idiom which makes it easy to distinguish the average Scandinavian melody from one of Spain or the other Mediterranean countries.

There are differences, however. In Swedish folksong the minor scales predominate; there are some tunes in the old ecclesiastical modes, but the modern diatonic forms are commonest.

The tunes are usually of small compass—rarely over an octave—with few accidentals and almost no ornamentation. In general the quality of preoccupation and restrained sorrow is reflected in music and words alike. Among the dancing songs the polka is the commonest. Its triple time is constant, but rhythmic figures and tempo vary from district to district. Only the rhythm resembles the Polish original; the generally slow tempos are Swedish, and the character of the dance has been changed completely. The dancing tunes are usually in major.

The music of Norway is more cheerful than that of Sweden. The major scale is commonest, though modal tunes are frequently encountered. Besides the heroic *kjaempeviser* there are many types of domestic song—of love and nature, of shepherds and cowherds, as well as satiric pieces. The Norwegians have a dance called the *springer* which is related to the Swedish polka, but their most conspicuous folkdance is the extremely vigorous *halling,* in which the men alternately stoop low enough to touch the floor and then leap high enough to touch with their toe a cap on the end of a stick.

Danish music has a characteristically continental flavor, with less individuality than other Scandinavian music possesses. There is a marked kinship with the folksong of Germany. Denmark is thickly settled and accessible; its culture has for centuries been absorbent. German musicians have been more important than native sons until very recently. And not only German musicians, but German books and songs have been imported. As a result the literary tradition has almost overpowered popular expression. Lyric folksongs exist in large numbers and run the gamut of subject matter —there are occupational songs, festival songs, rounds and singing games, love lyrics and songs of family life. But the hand of the conscious artist has lain heavily on the texts, and the melodies too have undergone a Germanization.

With the nationalistic awakening that took

place all over Europe in the nineteenth century, composers as well as folklorists turned to the treasures of national folk music. Grieg enjoyed particular success in using not only the Norwegian idiom, but also the actual folk melodies with which he became acquainted through the printed collections. He arranged a great many of them for piano, and has imparted a feeling of the primitive Norse ruggedness to almost all of his music. Beginning under the influence of German romanticism, as one critic has said, he renounced all European conventions in order to serve the muse of his own folk. And Grieg is only one of many Scandinavian musicians about whom this might be said.

Folksong is not yet dead in Scandinavia. "Popular" music has supplanted it noticeably in thickly populated districts, but in the countryside one can still hear the Norwegian alphorn, the *lur,* and at country dances the old tunes are still played on native varieties of harps (resembling zithers) and violins. Here is music of an unpretentious, simple kind, far removed in idiom from the volatility of the Mediterranean or the Oriental rococo styles. It is less good-humored than the folksong of Britain, less mysterious than that of Finland. But its very simplicity is one of its most genuine charms.

The Swedish songs in this collection should be termed popular rather than traditional. Their melodies are perhaps older than the nineteenth century, but the Swedish words were added by professional poets after the manner in which Burns and Thomas Moore popularized Scotch and Irish folk music by furnishing their own poetic texts to traditional airs. The poems for "Come, Pretty," "All Day While I'm at Work," and "Perhaps When Lilies Bloom" are by Lundquist, "Värmeland" by Anders Fryxell, and are little more than a century old. The first six of the seven songs are widely known and are published in all the modern collections much as Stephen Foster's work appears in American songbooks. "I Sit Alone" is a song of Swedish Finland, and like "Come, Pretty" and "Joy in Heaven" is in syncopated 3/4 time, the Swedish version of the polka. Aside from Fryxell's patriotic hymn praising Värmeland (or Warmland) in western Sweden, and the religious "Joy in Heaven," the lyrics are conventional love songs, with greater individuality and depth in the melancholy native melodies than in the sentiments expressed by the words.

The same conventions and traditions apply to the Norwegian popular songs. Two of the four here included are in the polka dance rhythm, and their texts are by known poets: "Homecoming from Summer Pastures" is by E. Storm, "Thank You, No!" by Hans Allum. In most modern collections "A Girl Fifteen" is printed with J. Olafson's poem "Ja hjemme" (Homeland). Here we have reunited it to its traditional dialogue text. Two of these are wooing songs in dialogue, the third a very attractive autumn song, reminiscent of the simple peasant life depicted at the beginnings of Gray's "Elegy." "Cowherd's Song" is an interesting peasant's song, based largely upon the natural tones of the *lur* or mountain horn. As is common in this sort of folksong, the cows (or goats) are called by name. Indeed, the cowherd's song took its rise as a practical aid in the task of calling the animals in after the day on the hillside. Musically the piece has all the good humor of a Tyrolean song without any of its superficial fluency.

Of the two Danish examples, "Good Evening, My Pretty" is a wooing-duet in nineteenth-century style. "Osborn Snare's Courtship," much older, is an example of the Danish ballad that was so influential and important in literary history. It is a fairly long poem and the last stanzas must be summarized for want of space. In its courtship text it is related thematically to the English riddling ballad which is mentioned in the note to "Go No More Arushing."

I Sit Alone

I sit a – lone, all my friends are gone, All the
ma – ny friends, and the one so dear. I feel a pain in my
in most heart He has gone a – way, he leaves me here.

Oh listen well, all you blooming girls,
All you girls who walk in the paths of joy,
Beware, beware, shun you vanity,
For a girl who's vain can't keep a boy.

Jag sitter ensam och är förskjuten
Av vänner mång', men av en så kär,
Och detta vill nu mitt hjärta såra
Att bliva så förskjuten här.

Ack hör ni kära flickor alla,
Ni som på glädjens stigar gå,
Låt icke högfärd er överfalla,
Dot är en lott, som skattlös går!

Värmeland

And when you go awooing, it's there that you should go,
To Värmeland, my friend—there's nowhere better,
In Värmeland, our maidens are true gifts of God.
So find one, and do your best to get her.
But if you would woo there, cast cares all away!
Our girls like sunny faces and hearts always gay.
So smile, boy! Or not a girl will have you.

In Värmeland a young lad is always gay and proud;
The wide world holds naught that can affright him.
The King commands—he's ready, and marches proudly off,
With sword-gleam and cannon-flash to light him.
Did thousands beset him, his spirit would rejoice;
No fear he'd feel, but fight still, and know no other choice
Than perish or win the fight with honor.

Will he not fight with courage, with courage and joy,
Will he not his young life's blood shed gladly,
Who knows at home his mother is kneeling in prayer,
His sweetheart beside her sighing sadly,
A true Varmeland's maiden, pure affection in her eyes?
The King commands—he's ready, and she shall be the prize
Of vict'ry—and shall he then not conquer?

Ack Värmeland, du sköna, du härliga land!
Du krona för Svearikes länder!
Och komme jag än mitt i det forlovade land,
Till Värmland jag ändock åter vänder.
Ja, där vill jag leva, ja, där vill jag dö:
Om engång ifrån Värmland jag tager mig en mö,
Så vet jag aldrig jag mig ångrar.

Ja, när du en gång skall bort och gifta dig, min vän,
Då skall du till Värmeland fara:
Där finnes nog Guds gåvor med flickor kvar igen.
Och alla ä de präktiga och rara.
Men friar du där, så var munter och glad!
Ty muntra gossar vilja Värmlandsflickorna ha:
De sorgsna, dem ge de på båten.

Och värmlandsgossen han är så stolt och så glad,
Han fruktar för intet uti världen.
När konungen bjuder, så drager han åstad
Bland kulor och blixtrande svärden.
Ja, vore det fiender i tusendetal,
Han ej dem alla fruktar, han vill ej annat val
Än dö eller segra med ära.

Och skulle han ej strida med glädje och med mod
Och livet sit våga, det unga?
Där hemma sitter moder och beder för hans blod
Med bruden, den älskade, unga,
En Värmlandsflicka, så huld och så skön!
För kung och land han strider, och hon skall bli hans lön·
Ho kan honom då övervinna?

7

Come, Pretty

What's the use of griev – ing, though the world's de – ceiv – ing?

Grief can – not help, the world's made that way. One girl does not want me—

shall I let that daunt me? No, nev – er! I'll be gay.

8

What's the use of grieving, though the world's deceiving?
Pretty she is, and merry she'll be!
Though she'd never say it, those bright eyes betray it—
She's waiting there for me.
Well, sweet-and-twenty, see, here I come.
Yours I will be, my little sugar-plum.
What have you to fear, girl? Wipe away that tear, girl!
Come, pretty, take my hand!

Jag tror jag får börja överge att sörja,
Fast hela världen står mig emot.
Fast än en flicka gjorde mig olycka,
Ändock är jag vid gott mod.
Fägringen, den du bär på din kropp,
Den livar hela kärleken opp.
Ögonen dina, täcka och fina, fötterna gå i dans.

Jag tror jag får börja överge att sörja,
Flickan hon bliver munter och snäll.
Fin som en blomma vill hon till mig komma
Flickan väntar uppa mig.
Hjärtungen lilla, här har du mig,
Aldrig i världen sviker jag dig.
Inte ska du gråta, vi ska bli så såta,
Lägg du din hand in min.

Joy in Heaven

Hearts here know it who have heard soft spir – it voic – es chid – ing.

Turn away, call your roving thoughts, let them linger there!
Tell your heart he who clings to earth only clings to care.
Yet above, flowers perfect joy, peace there has her abiding.
Listen, you will hear the voices, spirit voices chiding.

Glädjens blomster i jordens mull, ack visst aldrig gro.
Kärlek själv ju försätlig är för ditt hjärtas ro.
Men därovan för hopp och tro blomstra de evugt friska.
Hör du ej, hur andar ljuvt om dem till hjärtat viska?

It Cannot Be

My dear, I tru – ly love you, and will for all my life. How hard for me to know, then, you may not be my wife. Ah yes, I know you pro – mised that you would wait for me. But

pov – er – ty still dogs me, my dear, it can – not be!

I wish I could describe it, that you could feel my woe—
A sorrow known to many, which many more must know.
For one who's lost a sweetheart will not find joy again:
He knows the height of sorrow, he knows the depth of pain.

Av hjärtat jag dig älskar i all min levnadstid,
Men det kan jag väl tänka, jag får väl aldrig dig.
Själv du mig haver lovat, att du skall trogen bli,
Men jag är allt för fattig, det kan ju aldrig ske.

Ack, om jag kund' beskriva den kärleken så svår,
Som mången väl kan bära uti sin levnads år.
Den som sin vän bortmister, sin glädje mer ej får,
En sådan sorg och ängslan all annan övergår.

All Day While I'm at Work

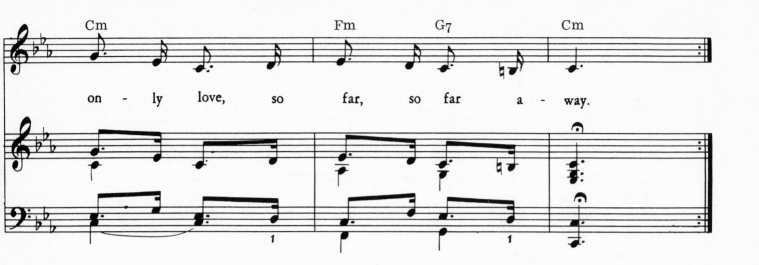

on - ly love, so far, so far a - way.

So night and day, and day and night, are yours and only yours.
Oh will the time yet come, love, when day and night are ours?
You are so far away, love, you are so far away.
The night is all too long, my love, and all too long the day.

Om dagen vid mitt arbete är du uti mitt sinn',
Om natten, då jag sover, är du uti min dröm.
Om morgen då jag vaknar, vem saknar jag väl då?
Jag saknar enda vännen, som är långt härifrån.

Perhaps When Lilies Bloom

have no mind for griev - ing, but grief holds me fast. I

hope he still may come, though the sum - mer has passed. One

year, or two may end all my sigh - ing. Per -

The days we spent together, I live in them yet.
But he was happy too, and can he, then, forget?
One year, or two, may end all my sighing.
Perhaps when lilies bloom,
Perhaps then he will come,
For love once born is ever long adying.

Och inte vill jag sörja och sörjer ändå;
Han kommer väl igen om ett år eller två,
När liljorna de blomstra i marken.
Han kommer väl igen, min hjärtans lilla vän.
För kärleken slutar så sena.

A Girl Fifteen

oth - er thing, She thinks of no - thing but a

wed - ding ring, none re - fus – es, none re - fus – es.

Girl: A boy at twenty, he makes me sick, always grumbles, always grumbles!
He'll jilt a beauty to play a trick, cut a tumble, cut a tumble.
But ten times "No", then you'll see him change,
He's always mooning now, it's very strange, now he's humble, now
    he's humble.

Boy: I want to marry, we think alike. Shall I take you, shall I take you?
Now don't be frightened, I'll never strike, beat or shake you,
    beat or shake you.
I may get cross, but I promise you
There's one thing, pretty pet, I'll never do—that's forsake you,
    that's forsake you.

Girl: If I don't take you, some other maid sure will catch you, sure will
    catch you.
You say you're gentle, I'm not afraid—better snatch you, better snatch you.
So now it's done, I will be your wife,
And I will love you truly all my life. So I match you, so I match you.

Guten: Når gjenta bare blir femten å, har a nykker, har a nykker!
Men blir a tjuge å frier får, gjør a sig lekker, gjør a sig lekker.
Men går a ogift i ti år te,
Så må du tru me, du ska få å se, ho samtykker, ho samtykker.

Gjenta: Så højt en onkar paa tjuge å, setter krasen, setter krasen,
Ta beste gjenta, i bygda går, jammen blås 'en, jammen blås 'en.
Men når han ti gange "nei" har fåt,
Så må du tru me, han e ikkje bråt så fjåsen, så fjåsen.

Guten: Nå enka mister sin fyste mann, kan a gråte, kan a gråte,
Ja, som ho reint var ifra forstand, kan a låte, kan a låte.
Men kom dær bare en frier da,
De blei'nte lenge, før ho sa ja, på en måte, på en måte.

Gjenta: En enkemann, som ve grava står, må vi æra, må vi æra,
For brura hass sytten, atten år ska jo være, ska jo være.
Han må ho mora ei lita stönn,
Om så han sju alens lange hønn, skulle bæra, skulle bæra.

Homecoming from Summer Pastures

20

glad to go, the cow to barn, the boy to house.

Farewell fields our cattle grazed, where, watching them, I sat and sang.
Farewell woods, my horn who heard, and sweetly with its echoes rang.
Farewell elves who haunt all the forest—better take our hut, live inside!
Winter winds will soon blow cold, and winter snows will soon lie wide.

Dairymaids and dairymen, the village calls—so down the hill!
Harvests done and grain is threshed, and all the cows can eat their fill.
In our village now roar the ovens, baking welcome-bread—how we'll feast!
Ended all the summer's toil, and home we go now, man and beast.

Os ha gjort ka gjerast skulde, y-sta ost å kinna smør,
Nå står att å kløyvja øykjom, setja lås for sæterdør.
Korkje finst dæ meire føe her for heie hell for Krist:
Gla æ' os, os slepp åt bygden, meire gla æ' kue vist.

Farvæl mork, som fænan gnågå, der e gjætte mangein gång!
Farvæl skog, som ofte ljoma tå min lur å stut åm sång!
Farvæl hulder, som der budde! Fløyt nå du 'ti sale inn:
Vinters ti ær ilt å liggje ute bå for vær å vinn.

Kom nå alt, 'ti sætre finnas, kom å følg åt bygden ne,
Heile jore æ' na røjugt, kvart eit strå høyr fænan te;
Skond døk', folkje venta heime, bufærslefsa vil døm hå.
Hær æ' intje meire gjera; folk å fæna, læt os gå!

Thank You, No!

"When I once make up my mind to wed, boy, I'll make sure the girl's a tho-rough-bred, boy. I will nev-er bind me till the day I find me One who'll let me drink my-self to bed, boy. Fill the

glass, boy, let it pass, boy, Tell me, do I look as green as grass, boy?"

"You, Marie, I rather think you'll do, girl.
Do you think I'd be the man for you, girl?
I have cows and pullets, pots and pans and skillets,
I can make enough to keep us two, girl.
I'm a man, girl, and I can, girl!
Take a winner, not an also-ran, girl!"

"Thank you, no! I don't believe you'll do, boy,
Go and find some other girl to woo, boy.
I will never bind me till the day I find me
Someone much more like a man than you, boy,
Find the right boy, not a bright boy,
But at least a sober one! Goodnight, boy!"

Jæ sku au ha løst t'å jifte mei san,
Når jæ traf ei jente rekti grei,
San, slik ho ente ville
Låte vontå ille,
Anten så jæ drekker heller ej, san.
Skjenk en dram san!
Tå mæ skam, san!
Fa'r di mange slike gutter fram, san.

Den som jæ skæ ha, må væra rar, san;
For jæ sjøl er en aparta kar, san!
Ho skæ kunne gjøre,
Hå de kommer føre,
Å så ta'r jæ ei, som pæing har, san.
Skjenk en dram, san!
Faa mæ skam, san!
Ta'r di mange slike gutter fram, san.

Hør du Mari, jæ vi fri te dei, san.
Dæsom du vi ha en kær som jei, san.
Jæ har kuer, sauer,
Gryte, fat å trauer,
Du maa tru jæ er'nte bare lej, san.
Jæ er'n kær, san,
Bytter mær, san,
Dæfor jifter jæ mæ som en kær, san.

Jami huen er'u kær i kvæl, san!
Men jæ vil å ældri ha dæ læl, san!
Du er grom t'å kjyte,
Å kan rækti skryte,
Men jæ blåser a det heile svæl, san.
Fy da Mass, san!
De er fjas, san!
Gå ifraa mæ me dit frieras, san.

Cowherd's Song

So lokka me over den myra
Te role haug, te role haug,
Kom alle dei underle dyra,
Kom ku, kom kælv, kom kjyra,
Kom Raute, kom Skaute, kom lækkete Kari,
Kom Kappelans Marit, kom Ronkebu Kjersti,
Kom Kjølums Berte, kom Hullabrand.

Osborn Snare's Courtship

The King and old Sir Os-born once Were drink-ing the sparkl-ing red wine. They drank red wine and they drank black mead, And all the while Sir Os-born talked of Kris-ti - na.

"O King of Denmark, grant this boon
And give me your daughter so fair."
"My daughter fair, she is still a child,
And all too young for stitching, little Kristina."

"So young she is, she'll quickly learn,
Then give me your daughter so fair."
Sir Osborn rode to the market town,
And silks he bought in plenty, all for Kristina.

"O nurse, good nurse, come counsel me,
This silk here was sent me to sew."
" 'Twas sent you, child, to make mock of you.
Sew not a stitch upon it, Princess Kristina."

The Princess cuts out a knight's tunic. On one side-seam she embroiders a fish swimming in a rushing stream, on the sleeve fifteen girls dancing in a ring, over the heart fifteen knights with drawn swords. When Sir Osborn sees it, he sends to tell her that her sewing is so fine that he will reward her with his hand. She answers that she will give him hers whenever he can swim to her across the embroidered stream.

Dankonning og Herr Asbjørn Snare
De drikke Vinen den klare.
Og skoven staar saa herlig grøn,
Den Sommer og den Eng saa vel kunne sammen.

De drikke Mjød, og de drikke Vin,
De snakked saa meget om liden Kirstin.
Skoven staar herlig og grøn,
Den Sommer og den Eng saa vel kunne sammen.

Dankonning! hør, hvad jeg siger jer,
I give mig Kirstin, eders Dotter kær.
Skoven staar herlig og grøn,
Den Sommer og den Eng saa vel kunne sammen.

Liden Kirstin hun er kun Aarene ti,
Eders Hofklæ'er hun hverken kan skær eller sy.
Skoven staar herlig og grøn,
Den Sommer og den Eng saa vel kunne sammen.

Liden Kirstin er ung, hun kan vel lære,
I give mig hende med Ære.
Skoven staar herlig og grøn,
Den Sommer og den Eng saa vel kunne sammen.

Herr Asbjørn rider til Ribe By,
Der køber han Silke og Sindal ny.
Skoven staar herlig og grøn,
Den Sommer og den Eng saa vel kunne sammen.

Han køber Silke og Sindal rød,
Det sender han alt til den ædle Mø.
Skoven staar herlig og grøn,
Den Sommer og den Eng saa vel kunne sammen.

Det første liden Kirstin hun Sømmen fik,
Straks ind til sin Fostermo'er hun gik.
Skoven staar herlig og grøn,
Den Sommer og den Eng saa vel kunne sammen.

Kær Fostermo'er! I kende mig Raad,
Sømmen hun blev mig sendt i Gaar.
Skoven staar herlig og grøn,
Den Sommer og den Eng saa vel kunne sammen.

Hør du, liden Kirstin, skik Sømmenfra dig,
Hun er dig sendt til Spot, tro mig!
Skoven staar herlig og grøn,
Den Sommer og den Eng saa vel kunne sammen.

Liden Kirstin hun ganger i Lønkammer ind,
Saa skar hun Sømmen alt efter sit Sind.
Skoven staar herlig og grøn,
Den Sommer og den Eng saa vel kunne sammen.

Hun satte sig paa Sømmestol,
Hun sømte imod den klare Sol.
Skoven staar herlig og grøn,
Den Sommer og den Eng saa vel kunne sammen.

Hun syed i hans Side-Søm Fisken,
Som skrider i striden Strømm.
Skoven staar herlig og grøn,
Den Sommer og den Eng saa vel kunne sammen.

Hun syed over hans Hærde femten
Ridd're med dragne Sværde.
Skoven staar herlig og grøn,
Den Sommer og den Eng saa vel kunne sammen.

Hun syede i hans Ærme en Krans af femten
Jomfruer i en Dans.
Skoven staar herlig og grøn,
Den Sommer og den Eng saa vel kunne sammen.

Nu er Sømmen syet og skaaren,
Krist give, den var nu hjembaaren!
Skoven staar herlig og grøn,
Den Sommer og den Eng saa vel kunne sammen.

Det svarede Jomfruens egen Svend:
Saa gerne bær jeg Sømmen hjem.
Skoven staar herlig og grøn,
Den Sommer og den Eng saa vel kunne sammen.

Det første, Herr Asbjørn Sømmen saa:
Herre Krist signe de Fingre smaa!
Skoven staar herlig og grøn,
Den Sommer og den Eng saa vel kunne sammen.

Meldte det Jomfruens egen Svend:
Hvad gi'er I den Jomfru til Sømm'løn igen?
Skoven staar herlig og grøn,
Den Sommer og den Eng saa vel kunne sammen.

Hvad andet skuld' hun have til Sømmeløn
End mig selver, en Ridder saa skøn!
Skoven staar herlig og grøn,
Den Sommer og den Eng saa vel kunne sammen.

Hjem kom den Smaasvend, han sagde vel:
Den Ridder vil have eder selv.
Skoven staar herlig og grøn,
Den Sommer og den Eng saa vel kunne sammen.

Bed Ridd'ren sejle over Aa;
Ret aldrig skal han faa min Tro.
Skoven staar herlig og grøn,
Den Sommer og den Eng saa vel kunne sammen.

Good Evening, My Pretty

"Good eve - ning, my pret - ty! So now your love's a sol - dier, I'm

sor - ry, my girl." "O yes, he's gone a sol - dier, and

I must walk a - lone now. My heart is oh so

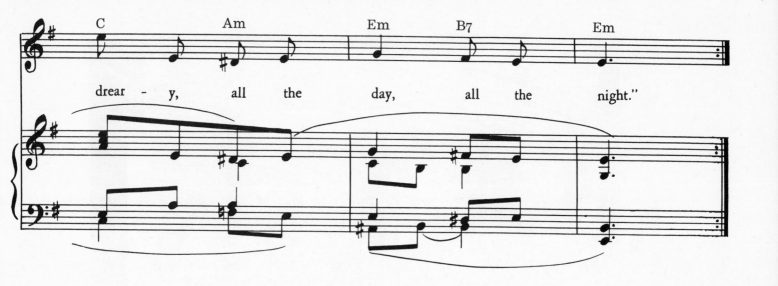

drear - y, all the day, all the night."

"Forget him, my pretty. You'll see he'll find another, wherever he goes.
For when a man's a soldier, his thoughts are always roving,
And, maid or wife or widow, he will find one to love.

"I'll dress you, my pretty, in silk so fine and satin, in scarlet and red,
And rings of gold and silver, and slippers too I'll give you,
If you will be my sweetheart, all the day, all the night."

"Why, Hans, are you fooling? I can't believe you mean it!
      Go, leave me alone.
I cannot bear to hear you. As him I love, he loves me.
The day that I forsake him, may I lie in the ground."

God Aften, min Pige! Er Kjæresten bortgangen, beklager jeg dig.
Ak ja, han er bortgangen, og ene maa jeg vanke,
For ham maa jeg bære Stor Sorg og Uro!

Bryd du dig ei om hanem, han tager sig en Anden, udi et fremmed Land.
Soldaternes Tanke blandt Pigerne omvanke,
Hvorhende mon drage til Lands og til Vands.

Jeg klæ'er dig, min Pige, i Silken den fine, skarlagen saa rød;
Guldringene fine skal ogsaa vorde dine,
Naar kun du vil være Allerkjæresten min.

Det er vel ikke Andet, end Spot, som du taler, o Hans, her til mig.
Ja, hvis jeg det gjorde, og Kjæresten det spurgte,
Saa slog han mig rent ud af Tanker og Sind.

Nei, før jeg skulde svige den, jeg bær i mit Hjerte, den, jeg har saa kjær:
For skulde jeg give mit Liv under Knive,
Og lade mig begrave i Muld og i Jord.

German

UNDER A SINGLE HEAD it will be convenient to consider the folk music of German-speaking peoples in Austria, Switzerland and Germany proper, as well as the Teutonic districts of the Low Countries—the Netherlands, and the northern or Flemish half of Belgium. There are some interesting regional differences, notably a more sparkling gaiety in the South, and a witty, even cynical character in the districts bordering France. Taking these and other such variations for granted, what we say will apply to all the Teutonic areas.

By the time the Minnesingers in the twelfth century were copying the French troubadours and providing the gentry with long metrical romances of chivalric adventure, the German *Volkslied* was already beginning one of its greatest periods of development. Later the guilds of Meistersingers, with their correct but academic poetry, were the logical figures of decadence, and the future of poetry looked dark indeed. But by the end of the Middle Ages the folksong had blossomed forth into a popular expression of all the people held in common. We know from important chronicles of the fourteenth and fifteenth centuries that these traditional songs existed in great numbers. The fifteenth-century manuscript Lochheim Song-book in fact reproduced a large number of contemporary tunes.

With the Reformation, an important step was taken by Martin Luther which was to have a far-reaching effect on the musical future of Germany. Luther was a musician himself and realized the importance of giving the people religious songs they could sing. He may have written the music to a few of his famous hymn texts, but we know that under his direction many more were set to adaptations of plainsong melodies, or to folk tunes familiar in the early sixteenth century. The influence of the noble but simple Lutheran choral was profound in Catholic as well as Protestant districts of Germany. Two centuries later Bach made more than five hundred harmonizations of these hymns, and they form the basis for his organ choral preludes and for many of the most moving sections in his passions and cantatas.

As the secular folksong continued on its way it became increasingly important as a source of inspiration for most of the German and Austrian composers from Haydn to Wagner. Indeed, in perhaps no other country of Europe is there so little essential difference between the idioms of folk and art music. Borrowings and imitations occur again and again in the works of classical and romantic composers. Bach introduced two folk airs into the *Goldberg Variations*. Schumann used "Als der Grossvater die Grossmutter nahm" in his *Carnaval*. Weber developed popular airs as theme and variations. Brahms quotes several student songs in his *Academic Festival Overture*. And Wagner, in choosing the subjects for his *Tannhäuser, Lohengrin, Die Meistersinger* and *Parsifal,* has drawn on the medieval poems of the Meistersingers, some of which had meantime been circulating as popular ballads.

The romantic revival, symbolized by the raptures which greeted the publication of Bürger's melodramatic literary ballad "Lenore," turned the attention of poets to the folksong. Like Burns and Scott, many of them polished fragments of folk poems and wrote others in conscious imitation of the Volkslied. As one critic has remarked, it is often difficult to tell when Goethe, Schiller, Uhland or Heine is borrowing from folk poetry, and when he is actually creating it anew, so deeply were they all steeped in the folk tradition. Bishop Percy's *Reliques of Ancient English Poetry* had awakened Herder in Germany to the existence of folksong which lay uncollected, and after his pioneering work and the subsequent publishing of the dilletante *Des Knaben Wunderhorn* (1805-8) by von Arnim and Brentano, the revival continued in full tilt. Many songwriters followed the contemporary poets in conscious imitation of the folksong style.

Side by side we have, then, in the nineteenth century, the genuine folksong and the *volkstümlich,* or folk-like, song. A conspicuous example of the latter is "Die Lorelei," with words by Heinrich Heine and music by Friedrich Silcher, one of the greatest of the folksong imitators. Schubert's "Der Lindenbaum" belongs to the type of art-song which, since it in not noticeably removed from the folk idiom, has passed into the same popular category.

In its general temper, the German folksong is midway between the solid seriousness of the Scandinavian and the ebullient vivacity of the Italian. Almost all its songs are in the major mode, and since the sixteenth century have been constructed in square four-measure phrases, with a complete absence of the peculiarities encountered in some neighboring countries. Modal scales are not to be found, nor has the Oriental influence of Turk or Gypsy penetrated into German districts. The melodic lines are rhythmically regular, ornaments are all but unknown, and the diatonic airs admit few accidentals. The effect of such regularity is to narrow the range of musical feeling. Thus a bright tune in major must serve for the unhappiest ballad as well as for a devil-may-care soldier's song. But this is not to say that the German folksongs lack variety. Fully half the traditional poetry is narrative, though as Entwistle points out, the *Volkslied* is primarily a lyric genre, and even the narrative pieces (such as our "Count and Nun") take a noticeably lyric turn. Yet among the pure lyrics the subjects run the gamut of love, war, tragedy, everyday work, in all their diversity. If there is a sameness, it is because the songs often stoop to sentimentality, seldom rise to nobility. In sum, the Teutonic folksong impresses us as familiar and *gemütlich,* warm rather than austere, homely rather than elegant.

In the South the *Ländler,* a precursor of the waltz, first became popular and spread over Germany. In Austria the *Ländler* were often associated with extemporaneous lyrics called *Schnadahüpfl*: during the dance it was customary for one after another in the company to sing impromptu quatrains for the amusement—or embarrassment—of those present. In other parts of Germany polkas and *Rheinländer* were sometimes danced to song. Switzerland and the Tyrol carry on the southern spontaneity, which reaches its Teutonic apogee with the *ranz des vaches* (the cowherd's song) and the yodel.

In the Low Countries, the Walloons are merely a continuation of France, with a distinctive patois speech but with all the French mannerisms and folk tradition. The Flemish and Dutch, however, whose language is an offshoot of Low German, are closely linked to Germany. Their land is thickly settled and the ordinary boundaries of city and country cannot be said to exist. Lacking the ordinary rural peasantry they have not developed a strongly nationalistic folk idiom, but import freely from Germany. Especially is this evident in the modern folksong of the eighteenth and nineteenth centuries. Earlier, when the Netherlands were relatively more powerful in Western Europe, their folksong was also more individu-

alized, as our examples from the period of the Renaissance show. Even then, however, they were an importing nation, and domesticated a quantity of English music and musicians.

"Rose Garden" and "Now We Must Part" are among the forty-nine "folksongs" arranged for solo voice by Brahms. The composer seems to have understood the essential qualities of these airs, and unlike Haydn and Beethoven in their arrangements of Scotch and Irish songs, Brahms avoids heavy chord clusters and bravura ornamental passages. He is perhaps given to too much chromaticism, and the accompaniments all bear the stamp of his individuality. Moreover, Brahms' inability to distinguish folk airs from composed tunes is as noticeable here as in his Hungarian dances (almost none of which are based on genuine folk melodies). The poem of "Rose Garden" is of the "Gather ye rosebuds while you may" genre; the symbolic meaning of the rose imagery is inescapable, and recalls Goethe's familiar "Heidenröslein." "Now We Must Part," an amorous "nightsong," was first collected near Bonn and but a short distance from Cologne. Its melody seems to be nineteenth century, but the words may be much older, if the detail of the watchman blowing for sunrise is not a conscious antiquarian touch of some forgotten German romantic poet.

"I Heard a Scythe" exists in many versions and is sung to a number of different tunes. The words first appeared in print in *Des Knaben Wunderhorn,* one of the numerous German collections of ballads and folksongs inspired by Percy's *Reliques.* Here again the words seem older than the melody.

"Count and Nun," the ballad of the young count and the nun was collected by the young Goethe while sojourning in Alsace in 1771. He gave it to his friend Herder, who used it to open his famous collection of folksongs (1778-9). The song was current in the Netherlands in the fifteenth century, and a fragment reveals its presence in Germany by 1540. But Goethe's is the earliest complete German version. Dr. Louis Pinck, who published a facsimile edition of Goethe's twelve Alsatian *Volkslieder,* states that this is the most widely circulated and most frequently sung of all the old ballads. Herder said of it, "It is sad and moving; in its simplicity it approximates a hymn." The word "Venetian," which appears in some versions of the text, must allude only to the color of the glass, and not (as is usual in ballads) to a glass that poisons any liquid poured into it. As if to avoid an ambiguity, some texts have "Romish glass" or "cool wine from a glass," and one has the young count pouring a "glass of champagne wine."

"When Will You Come Again?" a song from the Odenwald near Heidelberg, is a rather recent example of an old folk motif, in which apparently impossible obstacles are overcome that love may conquer all. In ancient texts the supernatural is frequently encountered. Here the romantic atmosphere does not contain more than a suggestion of possible tragedy, and the solution is one, not of ingenuity, but of accident. The text gives every appearance of being the work of an eighteenth- or nineteenth-century poet.

"The Dream," like "Rose Garden," is a symbolic love-poem. The landscape is unreal, the action unlikely. But the symbolism implicit in the verse gives it what meaning it has. The rosemary is a conventional symbol for misfortune, and its appearance in a rose garden is usually a sign of tragedy. The golden jug, with its "pearls" and "drops of red," is a symbol of the blood and tears which ominously prophesy tragedy. The poetry is, of course, the merest sentimentalism; and the rather recent tune is appropriate to it.

The tune of "Weep No More" was found in Westphalia, and dates from before 1820. The song has been popular in Switzerland, where it is sung in the Swiss-German dialect. Although the age of the poetry is not known,

it is in any case, as Erk and Böhme point out, older than Wagner's aria in *Tannhäuser.*

The three songs of the Low Countries are much older than those of Germany, and date from the seventeenth century or before. The first, the very popular Flemish ballad of Pierlala, introduces us to an entirely selfish and prankish figure not unlike Till Eulenspiegel. He is the spirit of irreverence; he is mercenary, rude, and conscience-free. People who cross him are unlucky; but in spite of his misdeeds, the ballad allows him an eleventh-hour repentance, in order to close with a moral. The anxiety of Pierlala's friends over his death is reminiscent of the theme which Ben Jonson brilliantly developed in his play *Volpone.* Ernest Closson, in his *Chansons Populaires des Provinces Belges* (Brussels, 1905), points out that the ballad reduces the adventures of Pierlala from epic to burlesque proportions. The song apparently dates from the 1670's, when Louis XIV overran the Low Countries.

"Let Us Quaff," a seventeenth-century Dutch drinking song from J. Starter's *Friesche Lust-Hof* (1634), quickly became popular in England as a country-dance tune, and with the title "Argeers" appeared in the first edition of John Playford's *Dancing Master* (1650).

"A Dew from Heaven" is a Flemish Mayday song, and recalls the old custom whereby young men "planted" May greenery beneath their beloved's window on "May night." The narrative takes up the theme found also in the German "Now We Must Part." The watchman is present in both poems, but here adds a fresh sparkle by singing as he does to the blissful young man. For another song growing out of a similar set of circumstances, see the Bohemian "Swallows Are Flying." The poem, which is clearly the work of a practiced hand, appeared in the *Antwerpsch Liederboeck* (1544), and the tune, like many another good ballad and dance air, adorned the very moral *Den Boeck der Gheesteliicke Sanghen* (1631).

I Heard a Scythe

Oh, let it sigh, my darling; I pay it little heed,
For I have found a sweetheart all in the flowery mead.

If you have found a sweetheart all in the flowery mead,
Then I must stay here lonely, my heart is sad indeed.

Ich hört ein Sichelein rauschen, wohl rauschen durch das Korn,
Ich hört ein feine Magd klagen, sie hätt ihr Lieb verlorn.

Lass rauschen, Lieb, lass rauschen, ich acht nit, wie es geh.
Ich hab mir ein Buhlen erworben in Veiel und grünem Klee.

Hast du einen Buhlen erworben in Veiel und grünem Klee,
So steh ich hier alleine, tut meinem Herzen weh.

34

The Dream

Last night while I was sleep - ing, there came a dream to me: A bush stood in my gar - den, a bush of rose - ma - ry.

My garden was a graveyard, a grave my flower-bed,
And all the blooms had fallen, and all the leaves were dead.

To gather up the flowers, a golden jug I found,
Alas, it was too heavy, it shattered on the ground.

And many pearls poured from it, and many drops of red—
Oh, what have I been dreaming, O sweetheart, are you dead?

Ich hab die Nacht geträumet wohl einen schweren Traum,
Es wuchs in meinem Garten ein Rosmarienbaum.

Ein Kirchhof war der Garten, ein Blumenbeet das Grab,
Und von dem grünen Baume fiel Kron' und Blüte ab.

Die Blüten tät ich sammeln in einem goldnen Krug,
Der fiel mir aus den Händen, dass er in Stücke schlug.

Draus sah ich Perlen rinnen und Tröpflein rosenrot;
Was mag der Traum bedeuten? Ach, Liebster, bist du tot?

Rose Garden

Your gar - den grows so love - ly, girl! Please, may I walk there? And

may I see your ro - ses, girl, your ro - ses so fair? Why

pluck them not while spring is here? The fall is all too late. Your

love - li - ness has filled my heart why must you make me wait?

O lovely girl, O beautiful, so lone, so forlorn,
Who ever told your lonely heart to treat me with scorn?
Why may I not your garden see, why do you still say No?
Your loveliness delights my eyes. Pray, let me tell you so!

Erlaube mir, feins Mädchen, in den Garten zu gehn,
Dass ich dort mag sehen, wie die Rosen so schön.
Erlaube sie zu brechen, es ist die höchste Zeit,
Ihre Schönheit, ihre Jugend hat mir mein Herz erfreut.

O Mädchen, O Mädchen, du einsames Kind,
Wer hat den Gedanken ins Herz dir gezinnt,
Dass ich soll die Rosen, den Garten nicht sehn?
Du gefällst meinem Auge, das muss ich gestehn.

Count and Nun

The youngest one of those three Counts arose, as the ship sailed past,
And poured his love the cool red wine,
And poured his love the cool red wine,
All in a Venice glass.

"Why pour you out the wine so red, and know it is not for me?
The world I must leave, to a cloister go,
The world I must leave, to a cloister go.
God's handmaid I will be."

"And will you to a cloister go, and will you God's handmaid be?
Then go your way, and God you keep,
Then go your way, and God you keep.
Sad maids are not for me."

Now when the hour of midnight came, the Count dreamt a dream full sore;
He saw the sweet maid he loved so well,
He saw the sweet maid he loved so well,
Walk through the cloister door.

Summary of the other stanzas:
    The young Count rides to the convent. He asks to see the youngest
nun. She appears, clothed all in white, her hair cropped, her lips bloodless.
The Count sits down on a stone by the gate and weeps until his heart
breaks.

Ich stand auf einem hohen Berg, sah nunter ins tiefe Tal,
Da sah ich ein Schifflein schweben,
Da sah ich ein Schifflein schweben,
Darin drei Grafen sass'n.

Der aller jüngst', der drunter war, die in dem Schifflein sass'n,
Der gebot seiner Liebsten zu trinken
Der gebot seiner Liebsten zu trinken
Aus einem venedischen Glas.

Was gibst mir lang zu trinken, was schenkst du mir lang ein?
Ich will jetzt in ein Kloster gehn,
Ich will jetzt in ein Kloster gehn,
Will Gottes Dienerin sein.

Willst du jetzt in ein Kloster gehn, willst Gottes Dienerin sein,
So geh in Gottes Namen
So geh in Gottes Namen
Deinsgleichen gibts noch mehr.

Und als es war um Mitternacht, dem Grafen träumt's so schwer,
Dass sein herzallerliebster Schatz
Dass sein herzallerliebster Schatz
Ins Kloster gangen wär.

Auf Knecht, steh auf und tummle dich, sattl' unser beider Pferd,
Wir wollen reiten bei Tag und Nacht
Wir wollen reiten bei Tag und Nacht
Die Lieb ist reitenswert.

Und da sie vor das Kloster kam'n, wohl vor das hohe Tor,
Fragt er nach jüngster Nonne
Fragt er nach jüngster Nonne
Die in dem Kloster war.

Das Nönnlein kam gegangen in einem schneeweissen Kleid,
Ihr Haar war abgeschnitten
Ihr Haar war abgeschnitten
Ihr roter Mund so bleich.

Der Knab, er setzt sich nieder, er sass auf einem Stein,
Er weint die hellen Tränen,
Er weint die hellen Tränen,
Brach ihm sein Herz entzwei.

When Will You Come Again?

"But tell me when you'll come again, O dearest love of mine."
"Why, when it snows red roses, girl, and when it rains cold wine."

"Red roses never fall like snow, it never rains cold wine.
You mean you'll never come again, O dearest love of mine."

She laid her in the roses' shade, and there she fell asleep,
She slept and dreamt the snow came down and she lay buried deep.

But now the boy comes back again, now through the garden goes,
His steps are slow, he carries gifts, a jug of wine, a rose.

He sees her—heeding nothing else, he runs with might and main.
He trips . . . rose-petals fall like snow, cold wine comes down like rain.

Wohl heute noch und morgen, da bleibe ich bei dir,
Wenn aber kommt der dritte Tag, so muss ich fort von hier.

Wann kommst du aber wieder, Herzallerliebster, mein?
Wenns schneiet rote Rosen und regnet kühlen Wein.

Es schneiet keine Rosen und regnet keinen Wein,
So kommst du auch nicht wieder, Herzallerliebster mein.

In meines Vaters Garten legt ich mich nieder und schlief,
Da träumte mir ein Träumelein, wie's schneiet über mich.

Und wie ich nun erwachte, da war es lauter nichts,
Es war'n die roten Röselein, die blühten über mich.

Der Knabe kehrt zurücke, geht zu dem Garten ein,
Trägt einen Kranz von Rosen und einen Becher Wein.

Hat mit dem Fuss gestossen wohl an das Hügelein,
Er fiel, da schneit es Rosen, da regnet's kühlen Wein.

Now We Must Part

He stood beneath his sweetheart's window,
Beneath her window a song he sang.
His voice was high and clear and manly.
She heard his voice, from bed she sprang.

"Be still, be still, my heart's true darling,
Be still, my darling, why stand you there?
My father sleeps, and sleeps my mother.
Awake them not or ill we'll fare."

Then hand in hand they stood together,
And kissed each other, stood heart to heart,
Until the watchman blew for sunrise—
Alas, alas, they now must part.

"Now we must part—we're always parting!
I cannot bear it, it breaks my heart.
And not one hour and not one moment
Can I forget that we must part."

Soll sich der Mond nicht heller scheinen,
Soll sich die Sonn nicht früh aufgahn,
So will ich diese Nacht gehn freien,
Wie ich zuvor auch hab getan.

Als er wohl vor die Gasse trat,
Da fing er an ein Lied und sang,
Er sang aus schöner, heller Stimme,
Dass sein Herzlieb zum Bett aussprang.

Steh still, steh still, mein feines Lieb,
Steh still, steh still, und rühr dich nicht,
Sonst weckst du Vater, weckst du Mutter,
Das ist uns zween nicht wohlgetan.

Was frag ich nach Vater, was nach Mutter,
Vor deinem Fenster muss ich stehn,
Ich will mein schönes Lieb anschauen,
Um das ich muss so ferne gehn.

Da standen die zwei wohl bei einander,
Mit ihren zarten Mündelein,
Der Wächter blies wohl in sein Hörnlein,
Ade, es muss geschieden sein.

Ja, scheiden, scheiden über scheiden
Tut einem jungen Herze weh,
Dass ich mein schön Herzlieb muss meiden,
Das vergess ich nimmermeh.

Weep No More

love you, nev - er fear.

Lovely hawthorn-tree, how your beauty pleases me,
Fills my eyes, and fills my mind, nothing fairer could I find.
    Weep no more, my dear, I love you, never fear.

Lovely butterfly, I will love you till I die,
Love you, dear, with all my power, every day and every hour.
    Weep no more, my dear, I love you, never fear.

Lovely rosebud new, could I always live with you!
I love you and you love me, yours I am and yours I'll be.
    Weep no more, my dear, I love you, never fear.

Schönster Abendstern, ei, wie seh ich dich so gern.
Wenn ich dich von ferne seh, denkt mein Herz, du seist bei mir.
Schönste, weine nicht, ich bin verliebt in dich.

Schönste Tulipan, deine Schönheit lacht mich an,
'S ist kein schöne auf der Welt, die mein'm Herzen besser g'fällt.
Schönste, weine nicht, ich bin verliebt in dich.

Schönstes Röslein rot, will dich lieben bis zum Tod,
Will dich lieben aus Herzensgrund, will dich lieben Tag und Stund.
Schönste, weine nicht, ich bin verliebt in dich.

Schönstes Röslein mein, könnt ich doch gleich bei dir sein.
Du bist mein und ich bin dein, will keins andern lieber sein.
Schönste, weine nicht, ich bin verliebt in dich.

Pierlala

life be - fell, You now shall hear them sung full well. I sing of Pier - la - la, sa - sa, I sing of Pier - la - la.

So well his father loved the boy,
So well his mother too,
They said: "Our only son and joy,
Our wealth we'll leave to you.
Take care, then, son! For all we own,
It shall be yours and yours alone."
"That's good!" said Pierlala, sa sa,
"That's good!" said Pierlala.

"Go hang yourself then, father mine!
Your wealth will buy my wish,
Which is, to swim in beer and wine
As deep as any fish.
The noble life that I shall lead
When you are dead and gone indeed!
Can't wait!" said Pierlala, sa sa,
"Can't wait!" said Pierlala.

And when at last his father died,
Our joyous Pierlala
Called all his friends from far and wide
To bury his papa.
For dainties Pier cared not a rap,
He fed his friends on broth and pap.
"Good stuff!" said Pierlala, sa sa,
"Good stuff!" said Pierlala.

After the funeral, Pierlala throws his friends out of the house. He marries, gets into debt, and takes to haunting taverns and beating his wife. Finally, he abandons her and enlists in the army. But soon, tiring of a soldier's life, he deserts. Feeling death approaching, he makes his will and turns his face to the wall. He is buried, and his friends hurry to divide his property. But Pierlala was not really dead. He opens his tomb, returns to his house, drives out his friends, takes back his wife, and lives a sober life thenceforth.

Komt hier al' bij, annhoort dees klucht:
Het is van Pierlala,
Een drolig vestjen vol genucht,
De vreughd van zijn papa.
Wat in zij leven is geschied,
Dat zult gij hooren in dit lied:
'T is al van Pierlala, sa, sa,
'T is al van Pierlala.

Zoo zeer was Pierlala bemind
Van vaartje moertje t'saam,
Zij zegden: Hoor eens, lieve kind,
Ons een'ger erfgenaam,
Gij wordt haast meester van ons goed,
Daerom ziet wel toe wat gij doet!
'T is wel, zeij Pierlala, sa, sa,
'T is wel, zeij Pierlala.

Papatjen, maak u maar van kant,
Dat ik uw schijven heb;
Ik zal mij dragen heel galant
Gelijk een water snep.
'K wil met den bek in't nat ook zijn,
Altijd verheughd in bier of wijn.
'T moet op, zeij Pierlala, sa, sa,
'T is al van Pierlala.

Maar as me was den vader dood,
Och armen Pierlala!
Die heeft zijn vrienden al genood
Op't uijtvaart van papa.
Hij hielt niet veel van lekkernij,
Hij gaf ze t'eten pap en brij.
'T is bon, zeij Pierlala, sa, sa,
'T is al van Pierlala.

Let Us Quaff

The sweetest time for man or maid,
The happy time of youth is ours!
Come, let us spend it unafraid,
With songs and wine and flow'rs!
When age has strewn our heads with gray,
When years have withered all our youth,
Then must our pleasures fleet away,
Then we'll be sad in sooth.
But till then, maids and men, be we gay!
Let us clink, let us drink, till it's day!
Who says "enough" now? Quick, let us quaff now,
Rejoice, while yet we may!

Is diet niet wel een vremde gril?
'T sou hier goed haver saeijen zyn:
'T geselschap is dus wonder stil,
In 't midden vande wijn.
De wijn die yeders hart ontfonckt,
En alle swarigheyd verlicht,
Daer by sit men nu noch en pronckt
Met een beveynsd gesicht.
Eẏ waerom doch dus stom en bedeckt?
Door goe vreughd wierd de deughd noyt bevleckt.
Hey! wilt dat staken, en u vermaken
Met al wat lust verweckt.

Wy zijn in't soetste van ons jeughd,
In't allerschoonste van ons tijd;
Ey, dat wy die niet sonder vreughd
Dus klack'loos worden quijt!
Wanneer den grysen ouderdom
De groente von ons jeughd verdort,
Dan kommen all' onse lusten om,
Ons vreughd word opgeschort.
Dus wel an, laet ons dan, wylmen mach,
En de tijd sullix lijd, tot den dagh
Recht lustigh wesen, vreughd word ghepresen,
En't lachen in't ghelagh.

Tsa jonghmans of jongh-vrouwen, seght,
Aen wien ist dat de roemer staet?
Men sal over dien houwen recht,
Die hem niet omgaen laet.
Want ick weet een die dorstigh is
En garen drincken sou zijn deel,
Vermits hy heel aem-borstigh is,
En't drooght seer in zijn keel.
Drinckt het leegh, met en vegh, soo is 't wel,
D'elen baes, die word haes, daerom sel
Hy 't u wel na doen, en sich wat dra spoen,
Hy eyscht gants gheen uystel.

A Dew from Heaven

on - ly she would love me, I would be well a - gain.

Cold winter now is over, and joyous spring is here.
I see the flowers open, I see the leaves appear.
How pleasant now to wander in yonder leafy vale,
Where many birds make merry, where sings the nightingale!

I'll go and set a Maypole before my lady's door.
I'll give my love my promise to love her evermore.
I'll say, "My own true lady, I've brought in May to you—
Come, deck the pole with flowers, as maids are wont to do."

The lady never doubted, she let her lover in,
She brought him to her chamber, where love's true joys begin.
Awhile they lay there hidden, rejoicing—but not long.
The watchman blew for sunrise, the watchman sang his song.

The watchman sings: "If there is anyone in the house, he must leave
soon. It is almost dawn." The lover answers: "I hold a beautiful woman
in my arms. She has cured my heart's sorrow. I cannot go." The watchman:
"The sun is rising. You must part. I must sing my dawn-song. Beware,
knight! Go now—another time you can return."

Het viel een hemelsdouwe voor mijn liefs vensterkijn.
Ick en weet geen schoonder vrouwe, si staet int herte mijn.
Si hout mijn herte bevangen, twelck is so seer doorwont,
Mocht ic haer troost ontfanghen, so waer ic gansch ghesont.

Die winter is verganghen, ic sie des meis virtuit,
Ic sie die looverkens hangen, die bloemen spruiten int cruit.
In ghenen groenen dale, daer is ghenoechlic zijn,
Daer singhet die nachtigale ende so menich voghelkijn.

Ic wil den mei gaen houwen voor mijn liefs vensterkijn,
Ende schenken mijn liefs trouwe die alder liefste mijn,
Ende segghen: Lief, wilt comen voor u clein vensterken staen,
Ontfaet den mei met bloemen, hi is so schone ghedaen.

Tmeysken si was beraden, si liet haer liefsten in
Heymelic al stille in een cleyn camerkin,
Daer lagen si twee verborghen een corte wijle ende niet lanc,
Die wachter opter muiren hief op en liet, hi sanck.

Och, isser yemant inne, die schaf hem balde van daen,
Ic sie den dach op dringhen, al in dat oosten up gaen.
Nu schaft u balde van henen tot op een ander tijt!
Den tijt sal noch wel keeren, dat ghi sult zijn verblijt.

Och, swighet, wachter, stille ende laet u singhen staen:
Daer is so schooner vrouwe in mijnen armen bevaen;

Si heeft mijn herte genesen, twelc was so seer doorwont,
Och, wachter goet, gepresen, en makes niemandt condt.

Ic sie den dach op dringhen, tscheyden moet ymmer zijn,
Ic moet mijn dageliet singen, wacht u, edel ruyter fijn,
Ende maect u rasch van henen tot op een ander tijt,
Den tijt sal noch wel comen, dat ghi sult zijn verblijt.

British Isles

THE VENERABLE BEDE, in his *Ecclesiastical History of the English People* (731), tells us of the first English singer to be known by name. He was Caedmon, the cowherd of St. Hilda's monastery, who was unable to improvise verses, and who, in the evenings when his fellows were singing, would steal out for shame as the harp neared him, because he knew he could not sing. One evening an angel appeared to him in a dream and said, "Caedmon, sing me something." Caedmon protested that he did not know how, but the angel persisted, and said, "Sing me the creation." Whereupon Caedmon lifted his voice and sang nine simple lines of a poem on the beginning of the world. Thenceforth he had the gift of song, but he considered it a sacred blessing, and, Bede tells us, used it only for the glory of God and the good of his fellow-men.

This account is interesting in and for itself, but it also tells us that song was a well-developed art as early as the seventh century. We cannot here trace the history of English music systematically through the ages, but we must point to one very important example of folksong, the earliest that has come down to us. The familiar round, "Sumer Is Icumen In," is earlier than Chaucer, and is significant as being perhaps the oldest piece of music written in the modern major scale. It is also the oldest extant secular song in English, and the oldest round. This rather elaborate composition has been conjectured to be the work of a monk named John of Fornsete, but modern opinion has it that John recorded a popular folksong and to it added the sacred words (in Latin) which also appear on the manuscript. In any case, it is strange that this song is unique, that many similar examples have not come down to us.

The medieval popular ballad, which seems to have taken its rise in Denmark, spread over England and Scotland during the thirteenth and fourteenth centuries. These narrative songs must have been very numerous indeed during the period of their greatest vogue. But since they were a purely oral genre, transmitted from one generation to another without benefit of writing, we have only circumstantial evidence concerning them until the much later period when they were collected. These narrative songs cover a wide range of subject. Many of them tell of knightly adventure and are related to the long courtly romances sung by professional minstrels. Others concern contemporary nobility and reflect a primitive society of hardihood in warfare and love alike. There are riddling ballads, ballads of superstition and the supernatural, and many pieces of domestic happiness and tragedy. There is a whole cycle of ballads about Robin Hood.

It is due largely to a trivial episode in the life of Bishop Thomas Percy (1729-1811) that the survivals of the medieval ballads are so numerous. Once while visiting in a Shropshire house he noticed a servant lighting fires with loose papers cached under a bureau, and his curiosity led to his rescuing from complete destruction a manuscript containing a large body of traditional poetry. Percy's *Reliques of Ancient English Poetry* (1765), based on this manuscript, was a haphazard and unfaithful piece of editing, but was of prime importance in stimulating an interest in the old ballads. It gave rise to Sir Walter Scott's valuable *Min-*

strelsy of the Scottish Border and the many collections that followed it, culminating in the monumental work of Professor Francis James Child of Harvard, *The English and Scottish Popular Ballads.* This last is a collection of 305 ballads with their variants (following the method of the Danish scholar Gruntvig), and a full account of their many parallels in other European countries. Attention to the music has been unfortunately less satisfactory. Old transcriptions of ballad melodies are not trustworthy, though they are valuable. Only with the work of the late Cecil Sharp can the accurate recording of folk melodies be said to have reached the scientific stage. Meantime, it must be noted in passing that the migrations to America in the seventeenth century transplanted ballads and folksongs to this country, whither they have gone their own way, developing fresh variants to accord with a new landscape and a different social organization. Many twentieth-century collections of old world ballads in America attest the vigor with which the tradition of folksong has been carried on in isolated communities of New England and the Southern mountains.

By the side of the traditional ballad, there was flourishing an urban variant known as the broadside ballad. In the sixteenth and seventeenth centuries the broadside was in its heyday of popularity, recounting in doggerel stanzas, to be sung to familiar tunes, the latest piece of sensational news—capture of desperate criminals, accounts of disastrous storms, tall tales of two-headed babes and women with piggish faces. And of course this journalistic note was supplemented by poems of obvious imaginative origin, by historical and political pieces. The diarist Samuel Pepys, who loved a ballad as life, made a large and valuable collection of which he was inordinately proud. These poems, printed on a single sheet and hawked about the London streets for a penny, drew upon well-known song and dance tunes, many of which were actually included on the broadsides themselves.

These popular tunes form a rich addition to the artistic madrigals and ayres of the Renaissance, England's greatest period of musical activity. Many of them are mentioned in the dramas of Shakespeare and his colleagues, and some of them, such as the "Willow Song," were actually sung in the plays. William Byrd, Dr. John Bull and Giles Farnaby wrote for the virginals intricate variations on "Greensleeves," "Walsingham," "The Hunt Is Up" and numerous other popular tunes.

In the seventeenth century when country dances became fashionable, the music publisher Playford began to issue *The Dancing Master,* which contained old fiddle tunes with directions for executing the dances to them. Playford's many editions are a voluminous record of the shifting styles from 1650 to about 1730, but even more important, many of the dance tunes were originally sung to popular ballads and folksongs which gave them their titles, and we are thus able to reconstruct the history of popular music much more accurately through the preservation of these tunes. Many of them were modal in the early editions and were later "modernized" to conventional major or minor scales, showing us that *The Dancing Master* was begun none too early for the preservation of the tunes in something like their original form.

Such collections of songs as Thomas D'Urfey's *Wit and Mirth: or, Pills to Purge Melancholy* (complete edition 1719-20) again turn to popular airs for many of the racy poems that fill the six-volume work. But the greatest impetus to the revival of folk music came with John Gay's *Beggar's Opera* (1728). Italian opera had been the rage in London for some time, and in a moment of disgust with the artificialities of the rococo Italian style, Gay conceived the perfect antidote—a stage full of beggars and highwaymen, singing not elaborate coloratura arias but simple songs whose unpretentious melodies were folk tunes familiar as ABC to the Englishman. *The Beggar's Opera* was an instant success and caricatured the Italian opera out of England for a time. The stage was thenceforth full of ballad operas. Besides Gay's *Polly,* London was offered *The Cobbler's Opera, The Jovial Crew, The Village Opera, The Grub Street Opera,* and scores of others during the next generation.

Despite the very active presence of folk music in the eighteenth century, Dr. Burney in his *History of Music* (1776-89) professed to find secular and popular music very "circumscribed" in England. Doubtless his extravagant love of the Italian school kept him from looking deeply into his native music. At any rate, he constantly belittled the work of his countrymen, criticizing not only their taste but their musical ability. Burney's strictures led William Chappell early in the nineteenth centry to an original study of popular music, and especially of ballad tunes. His researches were patient and exhaustive, and his *Popular Music of the Olden Time* (1855-59) is not only an astonishing book for its time, but is even today the standard work in its field. Chappell was particularly zealous to refute Burney's ill-founded claims; he not only advanced abundant proof of the vigor of England's musical life, but in his enthusiasm disputed the Scotch or Irish or Welsh origin of a number of tunes. His polemics were healthy, but occasionally mistaken. Yet he emphasizes the fact that a good deal of our folksong is British in the broadest sense, not merely English. Among our selections, for example, "The Girl I Left Behind Me" is familiar in Ireland, England and America. The Gaelic strain can be seen in Ireland, Wales and Highland Scots. The popular ballads flourished on both sides of the Tweed.

The music of Lowland Scots is a natural transition from that of England. The ballads of the late Middle Ages were perhaps more Scotch than English, but they circulated freely across the border in later years when the keen rivalry between the Percys and the Douglases had been somewhat softened by the union of the kingdoms. Our record of the folk music itself does not go very deeply into the past. There are several seventeenth-century manuscript collections of Scotch melodies, and a few tunes found their way into Playford's *Dancing Master*. But it was not until the next century that the music began to be recorded systematically. About the turn of the century a great craze for Scotch music swept England; theaters and music halls resounded with these northern song and dance tunes. English song writers and Italian music masters in London imitated the Scotch idiom, symbolized for them by the "Scotch snap" (actually found only in the Strathspey dance) and the pentatonic scale. Most of these imitations are transparent, but undoubtedly many a genuine Scotch folk tune was mutilated beyond recognition in order that it might seem Scotch to the casual listener.

Allan Ramsay, a wig-maker and poet of Edinburgh, attempted to make a collection of Scottish popular poetry, but his *Tea-Table Miscellany* (1724-32) is full of English art-songs and refurbishings of traditional native lyrics. Throughout the century the standards of editing were completely at variance with modern practices. Like Bishop Percy, the collectors valued elegance more than accuracy; they rewrote poems which seemed imperfect, suppressed any indecency or *double entendre,* and above all, gave no indication of the nature or extent of their tampering. These practices are the inevitable result of popularizing; even today the publication of authentic ballad and song texts is subject to surprising limitations, although our notions of accuracy have improved considerably.

The Scotch vogue was not merely an English fancy. It had its roots also in Scottish patriotism, and had the active encouragement and assistance of Robert Burns. When James Johnson, an Edinburgh engraver, proposed to collect the complete corpus of national music and poetry, Burns became interested, and for the glory of "Old Scotia" he became the chief contributor to the *Scots Musical Museum* (1787-1803). He wrote down folk poetry he had learned as a rich legacy from his mother, and as was usual in that time, polished, refined, even composed fresh verses for the collection and dug up some of the tunes which Johnson reproduced with a simple figured bass. The complete collection of 600 songs is a landmark in the history of popular music, and has not yet been superseded.

It did have an immediate rival, however. The publisher George Thomson, himself a Scotsman, became impressed with the richness of his nation's folksong at the St. Cecilia concerts in Edinburgh. His ideas of publication completely eclipsed in elegance those of his rival. Instead of reproducing the music simply, he hired the most eminent musicians of his day to provide accompaniments and opening and closing "symphonies." His fees attracted Pleyel, Kozeluch, Weber, Haydn and even Beethoven. Haydn alone set about half of all the airs in Thomson's six-volume Scotch series and the somewhat smaller Welsh and Irish collections that followed. For the words Thomson drew Burns away from the *Museum* to prepare about 120 poems for the Scotch volumes. Later he called upon Tom Moore, Joanna Baillie, Sir Walter Scott and other poets to translate and adapt the Celtic texts. Thomson's collections are more remarkable as curiosities than as repositories of genuine folksong; nevertheless, he and Johnson alike were sincere and spared no pains to provide the best collections possible within the standards of their time.

Where the folksong is straightforward and

robust in England, and colloquial and homely in the Lowlands, in the Scotch Highlands and the Hebrides we reach the bounds of the Celtic twilight, and the music rather approximates that of Ireland. For the people, whose ancestors once lived in Ireland, speak Gaelic and their music abounds with the sad mysteriousness typical of the Celt. Their music goes back to ancient druidical rites, and Marjorie Kennedy-Fraser, who has made recent important collections of the Hebrides survivals, is inclined to date the earliest extant music as at least two thousand years old. In ancient days, harpers improvised songs to their own accompaniment, and the three-fold accomplishments of poet, singer and instrumentalist were highly developed in the early centuries of the Christian era. Besides the harp, Scotland has the bagpipe, but only for the past three hundred years has it supplanted the harp.[1] Its melodies are not, on the whole, suited to singing. But for Scottish dance tunes—the slow Strathspey and the fast reel—as for the martial *pibroch* and the funereal *coronach,* the bagpipe is unexcelled.

The songs of the Hebrides are especially valuable in that the western islands have been almost completely isolated from the outside world, and hence have preserved the folk music without the distortions which urban civilization has brought to the more accessible sections of the Scottish mainland. In the islands traditional song continues to be a constant accompaniment of every domestic activity. Mrs. Kennedy-Fraser has recorded a variety of *luinigs,* which are short, plaintive airs sung by women, especially when at their work. Spinning, weaving, grinding grain, fulling cloth, or making hay are all accompanied by these chants. And the men have their boating songs. The music

is characteristic of the old forms: modal tunes are the rule rather than the exception, and the rhythms are far subtler than we are accustomed to in our modern strictly accented measures. Peculiar to the Hebrides, and we may assume typical of the older state of Scotch Highland music, is the sadness of atmosphere which allows few tunes in the familiar major mode; typical also is the fondness for the pentatonic scales (scales which can be made on the black keys of the piano).

The spirit and atmosphere of the Celtic Scotch have been splendidly summed up by Kenneth MacLeod. "Passing strange," he says, "that drudgery and pain should rush into music as naturally as the sparks fly upward; that a girl milking a cow, an old dame spinning the wool, men rowing a clumsy fishing-skiff, a woman in tears because a seaman has been drowned—that such things should move the folk to song as easily as the dawn sets the lark trilling or twilight the mavis. To a race with soul, however, there is nothing common or tame in the whole range of life, from birth to death."[1]

The music of Ireland and Wales takes us back to the ancient world in which the harp was the supreme instrument and harpers were men of unusual ability and dignity. In both countries the harp is still cultivated; in both the tradition of folk music, whether extempore or traditional has not until recently been overshadowed by the work of the modern professional composer. Ireland is said by many critics to have the finest body of folksong of any nation. That it is known to a wide audience today is due in large part to the work of the popular poet Thomas Moore, who composed poems to a large number of traditional Irish harp tunes which had been collected by Edward Bunting, and sang them to great acclaim in Ireland and

---

[1] The bagpipe is by no means peculiar to Scotland, though it may have reached its highest development there. It is one of the oldest instruments of which there is any record, and has been common among the folk throughout Europe ever since the Middle Ages. It seems to have enjoyed a vogue in England before its period of popularity in Scotland began.

[1] Foreword to Marjorie Kennedy-Fraser's *Songs of the Hebrides,* I (London, 1909), xxxix.

England. Like Burns, he joined his own memorable, if sweetish, lyrics to folk airs many of which had no established texts; like Burns, also, he was associated with the publication of large numbers of his songs, for which, however, he received handsome sums. Unlike Burns, Tom Moore was not above adapting the melodic lines to suit his own lyrics; furthermore, it has been shown that he, or Sir John Stevenson who provided the Haydnesque accompaniments, suppressed the original modal character of many of the *Irish Melodies.* Yet despite the casual manner in which he treated his sources, he could not disguise the fine melodic character and emotional warmth of his Irish tunes. We can envy anyone's first hearing of "Believe me, if all those endearing young charms," or "The harp that once thro' Tara's halls," or " 'Tis the last rose of summer." When fresh, their melodies were unsurpassed, and if too much popularity has cloyed them, it can only be said that these are but a few of the 125 Irish songs which Tom Moore published.

In the Irish folksong with Gaelic words we can see the continuity of characteristics observed in the Scotch Highlands and the Hebrides. Similar occupational tunes abound, especially for milking, spinning and plowing, and the love song is of great importance. Sir Charles Villiers Stanford, who has asserted that the body of Irish folk music is the largest that exists, points out their great variety and calls attention to the presence of modal scales. The appearance of pentatonic scales in Irish music seems to him another example of musical kinship with the Highland Scotch.

Among the favorite Irish dances, jigs, hornpipes and reels are familiar. Robert Stewart says that many dance tunes in 6/8 time were originally marches, the Irish preferring the quick step of the 6/8 measure to the usual marches in common time. Among the tunes that Beethoven set for George Thomson's Irish collection, several seem to have been recalled by the composer in his Seventh Symphony, written soon afterward. Not only are the rhythms Irish—the first movement is in jig time while the last has been described as a "giant reel"—but some of the figures which Beethoven had developed in his accompaniment to "Kitty of Coleraine," for example, are followed very closely in the Symphony.[1]

The Welsh harpers are the descendants of the ancient Celtic bards whose work was subject to elaborate rules and existed in a high state of advancement even before Caesar conquered their then Gallic home. They extemporized heroic, lyric and satiric song to their own accompaniment and thus are to be related to the minstrels who flourished all over Europe at a much later date. The Welsh bard, like the Irish, was a revered individual and even in recent centuries has remained above the level of the mere entertainer. Until recently most of the Welsh folk music consisted of harp tunes, necessarily harmonic, as distinguished from the single melodic line of airs played on most other instruments. But Wales has always been a nation of singers, and in recent years old melodic songs have been discovered and collected in large numbers, after having been all but stifled by the force of the eighteenth-century religious revival which looked with disfavor on the secular words. John Wesley's remark that there was no reason why the devil should possess all the good tunes, may explain how some of these old folksongs came to be set to religious words.

The common Celtic origin probably accounts for the musical affinities of Irish and Welsh music, but Wales has preserved some of her old musical traditions uniquely. One is penillion singing, an extraordinary variety of vocal improvisation and poetic extemporizing. Accord-

---

[1] See James Travis, "Celtic Elements in Beethoven's Seventh Symphony," *Musical Quarterly,* XXI (1935), 255.

ing to the exacting rules of the North Wales contests, a harper plays a strain once to acquaint the singers with it. Then the contestants in turn invent stanzas, often with elaborate internal rhyme, while singing to the harper's accompaniment. They may not follow the melody, but must sing a counterpoint to it (and this may be in a highly contrasting rhythm). Obviously such impromptu performances do not, except by accident, develop any traditional song; but they are an example of the popular talent that exists in this musical country. The national celebration is the Eisteddfod, once the periodical meeting of Welsh bards to examine candidates for the various bardic degrees. In recent centuries the Eisteddfod has been devoted more and more to choral and other musical contests, though the poetic awards are still granted. Welsh choirs are renowned for their fine, vigorous singing, and of late a noticeable reintroduction of the old folksongs has been taking place.

With the exception of the first quatrain, which stands rather outside the atmosphere and subject-matter of the rest, "Go No More Arushing" is a riddle-song, one of the oldest types of folksong. The Child ballad No. 46, "Captain Wedderburn's Courtship," introduces these very riddles, along with many more, as young Grizey Sinclair tries to perplex the strange Captain Wedderburn who has come wooing. He answers all her riddles, and so gets Grizey for his wife. It seems clear that in the oldest form of such songs, the conclusion comes when the questioner is identified as the devil himself and a curse is thereby escaped. The romantic ending of the courtship ballads is, says Child, a more modern reshaping of the old tradition. In our present song the narrative element has entirely disappeared; versions of this sort exist in manuscripts of the fifteenth century and have survived to the present through oral tradition. With only slight varia-

tion in the riddles, but with an entirely different melody, the song has been popular in the Kentucky mountains. One version begins:

I gave my love a cherry that has no stone,
I gave my love a chicken that has no bone,
I gave my love a ring that has no end,
I gave my love a baby that's no cryin'.

An arrangement of the tune by Giles Farnaby, titled "Tell Me, Daphne," appears in the seventeenth-century *Fitzwilliam Virginal Book.*

"The Spring's Acoming" gets its title from the first line of a poem entitled "The Bath Medley," written by Tony Aston. The air, which he may also have written, appeared in the last edition of *The Dancing Master* (1728) and soon was used for songs in a number of ballad operas. In 1729 the music was printed, with Aston's voluminous patter choruses, in the first volume of a delightful work called *Watts' Musical Miscellany.* Our text follows Aston at the outset and then retires to less flamboyant lines than Aston uses to describe life at the fashionable eighteenth-century watering place. Aston's text continues in this vein:

Bliss past comparison, at Mr. Harrison's,
Dice are rattling, beaus are prattling,
Ladies walking and wittily talking;
Madam, the Medley is just begun.

Chappell in his *Popular Music of the Olden Time* says of Tony Aston that "his way of living was . . . peculiar to himself; resorting to the principal cities or towns in England, with his *Medley,* as he termed it, which was composed of some scenes of humour out of the most celebrated plays, and filling up the intervals between the scenes by a song or dialogue of his own writing."

"Sing Ovy, Sing Ivy" was one of hundreds of folksongs which Cecil Sharp and several co-workers unearthed during a collecting expedition through Hampshire county in the summer of 1905. It is a good-natured picture of a miniature farm, with each detail of the young farmer's year perfectly reduced to microscopic proportions. The tune is one of many modern English folktunes still sung in modal scales. This is in the Aeolian mode.

"The Wee Croodin' Doo" is a Scotch nursery form of "Lord Randall." This version was collected from a Lancashire woman in 1909, who had in turn learned it from her mother in Yorkshire. The collector, Miss Annie G. Gilchrist, points out that this version "is a good deal like that printed in Chambers' *Popular Rhymes,* as sung by Mrs. Lockhart, Sir Walter Scott's daughter, but the tune is not the same." "Lord Randall" is Child ballad No. 12. Child prints a number of "Croodin' Doo" versions, all of them Scottish. Our present text presumably came thence over the border to neighboring Yorkshire. "Lord Randall," called also "Lord Ronald," "Young Jimmy Randall," and so on, is one of the most widely dispersed of all the ballads. Besides its active life in America, versions of the story have been found in Italian, German, Wendish, Dutch, Swedish, Magyar, Bohemian and Catalan. The story in its usual form discloses a youth returning from his true love (here it is from a step-mother). He has been given eels (here a wee, wee fish) to eat, and the fate of the dog makes it clear that both have been poisoned. In the longer versions, his mother asks him what he will leave to each of his relatives in turn, and finally, what he will leave his true love:

> *"I'll leave her hell and fire; mother,*
> *mak my bed soon*
> *For I'm sick at the heart, and I fain*
> *wad lie down."*

In our version "croodin' doo" means "cooing dove."

"On a Bank of Flowers," supposedly Scottish, is by no means that. Nor is it a folksong. Burns, to whom the words are credited in John-son's *Scots Musical Museum,* rewrote an anonymous poem from Allan Ramsay's *Tea-Table Miscellany,* altering the amorous dalliance of Celia and a gentle swain, innocent though it is, to something even less exceptionable. The pseudo-pastoral is replaced by an artificial rural pair named Willie and Nellie who otherwise are indistinguishable from the originals. Burns, in other words, did not alter an English poem so that it became Scots; furthermore when he forsook dialect to imitate his English contemporaries he was seldom at his best. But the important thing is the actual origin of Ramsay's poem. It had been printed in *Watts' Musical Miscellany* (1729), with words by Lewis Theobald, one of the most prominent poets and editors of his day, and music by John Ernest Galliard, a German-English composer. There is more of the "British Grenadiers" than of Scotch heather in the tune.

"The Lea Rig," whose melody first appeared in print about the middle of the eighteenth century, was published in the first volume of Johnson's *Scots Musical Museum* with a fresh text by Robert Fergusson, which may have been based on the original words of the folksong. The song later appeared in the rival collection published by George Thomson, this time with a new version of the poem by Robert Burns in his best Scots dialect, and with a very florid Germanic accompaniment by Haydn. In the Burns version of the text which we reprint, the "lea rig" is the ridge left in grass at the end of a plowed field. The lover tells his love that he will meet her there in the twilight when the oxen (*owsen*) return weary from the field to be penned up for the night (*bught* is Scots for "pen" or "fold"). Burns adds a small stream (*burn*) and birch trees (*birks*) to the romantic charm of the *gloamin'* time.

Of the songs in our Scottish section, one is a reworking of an English art song, another a border ballad, another a Lowland Scots melody with a poet's words. With "Cuckoo of the Grove" we come to a genuine Highland product from further north. Our text is an adaptation of the Victorian translation from the Gaelic made by Thomas Pattison.

All five of our Irish songs are love ditties. Indeed, rare is the Irish song that does not speak of love. "Irish Girl" belongs to the popular class of soldier songs. This soldier found his love in southern Ireland and he sings of bliss; the next two songs grieve for the girl left behind when the troops have sailed for France. The last song in the section, "Roisin Dubh," whose words are based on a translation made by Thomas Furlong, differs from the others in that a political allegory is implicit in the text. In this sixteenth-century song, the rose symbolizes Ireland which will never be forsaken by her true friends.

"The Girl I Left Behind Me" has been the subject of a hot little controversy. It is claimed as an Irish tune on the ground that native harpers knew it early in the eighteenth century. It is claimed as an English tune on the ground that the original song beginning, "I'm lonesome since I crossed the hill," alludes to a military camp at Brighton, which would place its origin about 1758 or in the 1790's. Without arguing the question of priority, we can be sure of two things: it was regularly played by English military bands whenever naval vessels weighed anchor or soldiers were transferred from a post, and it was sung in Ireland to the poem beginning, "The dames of France are fond and free." Moreover, it was considered an Irish melody by Thomas Moore (though he was not overscrupulous about taking good tunes where he found them), and he set it to his own poem beginning, "As slow our ship her foaming track." The history of the song did not end there. About 1840 the author of

"The Lowbacked Car," Samuel Lover, wrote a charming lyric for the tune, calling it also "The Girl I Left Behind Me." The song with the "Brighton" words has been popular in the United States. For the dance call associated with an American fiddler's version of the tune, see Ira W. Ford, *Traditional Music of America* (New York, 1940), p. 211.

Thomas Moore included the air to "On and On" in his *Irish Melodies,* and, as was his custom, he replaced the original words with a poem of his own, "I wish I were by this dim lake." The "dim lake" refers to an "ancient haunt of superstition," Lough Derg, in northwestern Ireland. On an island in this lake was a cave famous as the legendary scene of St. Patrick's Purgatory. It became a shrine for pilgrims, and the wild, Gothic landscape plus the eerie damp and mist lent a romantic glamor to the otherwise forbidding scene.

"Come Rest in This Bosom," to the tune of "Lough Sheeling" is another of Moore's *Irish Melodies* with his own poetry and his customary alteration of the original air. The tune is also sung to a poem beginning "Adieu my loved harp."

"The Grey Old Stone" has been often translated into English, but by none as successfully as by John Oxenford. The title alludes to the historic battle of Bosworth Field in 1485, when Rhys Bodychen is supposed to have led his Angelsey men to and from the battle across a stone causeway that separated the island from Wales proper. The tune, probably later than fifteenth century, is one of those arranged by Haydn for George Thomson's collection of Welsh songs.

The other Welsh song has not the historical flavor of "The Grey Old Stone." It is a love song of pure unabashed sentiment, perhaps a bit overwrought for modern tastes.

The Spring's Acoming

Sing Ovy, Sing Ivy

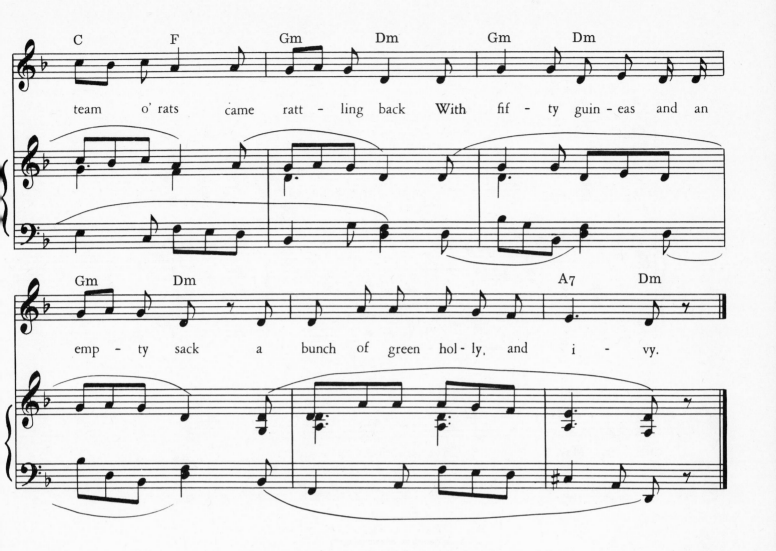

I harrowed it with my bramble bush—sing ovy, sing ivy
I harrowed it with my bramble bush—a bunch of green holly and ivy.

I sowed it with two peppercorns—sing ovy, sing ivy,
I sowed it with two peppercorns—a bunch of green holly and ivy.

I rolled it with a rolling pin—sing ovy, sing ivy,
I rolled it with a rolling pin—a bunch of green holly and ivy.

I reaped it with my little penknife—sing ovy, sing ivy,
I reaped it with my little penknife—a bunch of green holly and ivy.

I stowed it in a mouse's hole—sing ovy, sing ivy,
I stowed it in a mouse's hole—a bunch of green holly and ivy.

I threshed it out with two beanstalks—sing ovy, sing ivy,
I threshed it out with two beanstalks—a bunch of green holly and ivy.

I sent my rats to the market with that—sing ovy, sing ivy,
I sent my rats to the market with that—a bunch of green holly and ivy.

My team o'rats came rattling back—sing ovy, sing ivy,
My team o'rats came rattling back
With fifty guineas and an empty sack—a bunch of green holly and ivy.

Go No More Arushing

How can there be a cherry without a stone?
How can there be a chicken without a bone?
How can there be a ring that has no rim at all?
How can there be a bird that hasn't got a gall?

When the cherry's in the flower it has no stone,
When the chicken's in the egg it has no bone,
When the ring is in the making it has no rim at all,
And the dove is a bird without a gall.

On a Bank of Flowers

On a bank of flowers in a sum-mer day, For sum-mer light-ly drest, The youth-ful bloom-ing Nel-ly lay, With love and sleep op - prest. When Wil-lie wand-ring

Her closed eyes like weapons sheathed
Were sealed in soft repose;
Her lips, still as the fragrance breathed
It richer died the rose.
The springing lilies sweetly prest,
Wild, wanton kissed her rival breast;
He gazed, he wished, he feared, he blushed,
His bosom ill at rest.

Her robes lightly waving in the breeze
Her tender limbs embrace;
Her lovely form, her native ease,
All harmony and grace;
Tumultuous tides his pulses roll,
A faltering, ardent kiss he stole;
He gazed, he wished, he feared, he blushed,
And sighed his very soul.

As flies the partridge from the brake
On fear inspired wings,
So Nelly starting, half awake,
Away affrighted springs;
But Willie followed,—as he should,
He overtook her in the wood;
He vowed, he prayed, he found the maid
Forgiving all and good.

(Robert Burns)

The Wee Croodin' Doo

Oh, where have you been this live-long day, my lit-tle wee crood-in' doo? I've been to see my step-moth-er, mar-mee, oh make my bed noo!

And what did your stepmother give you to eat,
    my little wee croodin' doo?—
She gave me but a wee, wee fish,
    all covered with green and blue.

And what did you do with the bones of the fish,
    my little wee croodin' doo?—
I gave them to my wee, wee dog,
    marmee, oh make my bed noo!

And what did your dog when he'd ate up the fish,
    my little wee croodin' doo?—
He stretched his wee, wee limbs and died,
    marmee, as I do noo!

The Lea Rig

When o'er the hill the even – ing star Tells bught – in' time is near, my jo, And ow – sen frae the fur – row'd field Re – turn sae dowf and wear – y, O. Down by the burn, where scen – ted birks Wi' dew are hang – ing clear, my jo, I'll

meet thee on the Lea - rig, My ain kind dea - rie, O.

In mirkest glen, at midnight hour,
I'd rove, and ne'er be eerie, O,
If through that glen I gaed to thee,
My ain kind dearie, O.

Although the night were ne'er sae wild,
And I were ne'er sae weary, O,
I'd meet thee on the lea-rig,
My ain kind dreary, O.

The hunter lo'es the morning sun,
To rouse the mountains deer, my jo,
At noon the fisher seeks the glen,
Adown the burn to steer, my jo.

Gi'e me the hour o'gloamin' gray,
It makes my heart sae cheerie, O,
To meet thee on the lea-rig,
My ain kind dearie, O.

(Robert Burns)

Cuckoo of the Grove

roam - ing. I would touch her soft cheek, her name I would speak, As we

walked through the woods to - geth - er, And all through the night we would

laugh with de - light In our love and the sweet spring wea - ther.

I love her so well that no tongue can it tell,
I gaze at her face for hours.
Her cheek it is bright and her neck lily-white,
And her eyes are as soft as flowers.
Till they bear me away to sleep in cold clay,
All my thoughts to her go homing.
Ah, would I were now 'neath the sweet greenwood bough,
Hand in hand with my true-love roaming.

Irish Girl

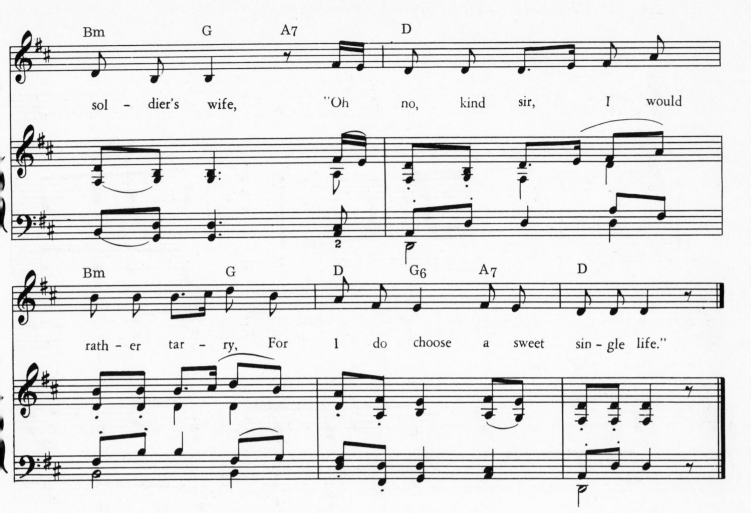

"You are the fairest of Irish maidens,
And you are fit, love, to be a queen.
I wish I was in some battle wounded
Before your sweet pretty face I'd seen.

"I wish I had you in Phoenix Island,
One hundred miles from your native home,
Or in some valley where none would find us,
You might incline, love, to be my own."

"You have not got me in Phoenix Island,
One hundred miles from my native home,
Nor in a valley where none can find me,
I'll not incline to be your own.

"Please do not tease me nor yet dispraise me,
Along with you I can never go.
So do sail over to where you came from,
And let me stay here for evermore."

The Girl I Left Behind Me

The dames of France are fond and free, And Flem - ish lips are wil - ing, And soft the maids of I - ta - ly, And Span - ish eyes are thrill - ing. Still, though I bask be - neath the smile, Their

charms fail to bind me, And my heart falls back to

Er - in's Isle, To the girl I left be - hind me.

For she's as fair as Shannon's side,
And purer than its water,
But she refused to be my bride
Through many a year I sought her.
        Yet since to France I sailed away,
Her letters oft remind me,
That I promised never to gainsay
The girl I left behind me.

She says, "My own dear love, come home,
My friends are rich and many,
Or else, abroad with you I'll roam,
A soldier stout as any.
        If you'll not come, nor let me go,
I'll think you have resigned me."
My heart nigh broke when I answered "No"
To the girl I left behind me.

For never shall my true love brave
A life of war and toiling,
And never as a sulking slave
I'll tread my native soil on.
        But, were it free or to be freed,
The battle's close would find me,
To Ireland bound, nor message need
From the girl I left behind me.

On and On

I wish I were on yon - der hill, 'Tis there I'd sit and cry my fill Till ev'ry tear would turn a mill— Oh, may God safe - ly guide you on! On, on, on, my dear,

I'll sell my rack, I'll sell my wheel,
I'll sell my only spinning wheel
To buy for my love a sword of steel—
Oh, may God safely guide you on!
    On, on, on, my dear,
    On you wander, on and on.
    All the while you wander, darling,
    I weep here.
    Oh, may God safely guide you on!

I'll dye my skirt, I'll dye it red,
And round the world I beg my bread,
Until my parents shall wish me dead—
Oh, may God safely guide you on!
    On, on, on, my dear,
    On you wander, on and on.
    All the while you wander, darling,
    I weep here.
    Oh, may God safely guide you on!

I wish, I wish, I wish in vain,
I wish I had my heart again,
And vainly think I'd not complain—
Oh, may God safely guide you on!
    On, on, on, my dear,
    On you wander, on and on.
    All the while you wander, darling,
    I weep here.
    Oh, may God safely guide you on!

But now my love has gone to France
To try his fortune to advance.
If e'er he comes back 'tis best a chance—
Oh, may God safely guide you on!
    On, on, on, my dear,
    On you wander, on and on.
    All the while you wander, darling,
    I weep here.
    Oh, may God safely guide you on!

Come Rest in This Bosom

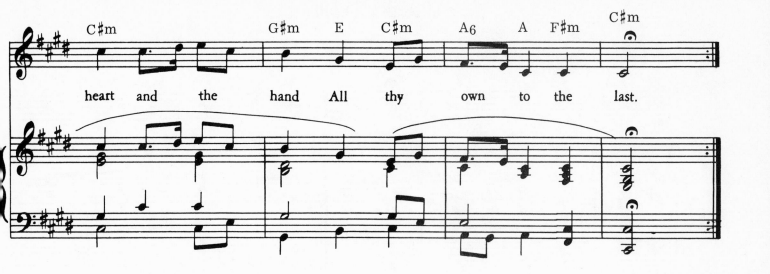

heart and the hand All thy own to the last.

Oh, what was love made for,
If 'tis not the same,
Through joy and through torments,
Through glory and shame?
I know not, I ask not,
If guilt's in the heart,
I but know that I love thee,
Whatever thou art!

Thou hast called me thy Angel
In moments of bliss,
Still thy Angel I'll be
'Mid the horrors of this,
Through the furnace, unshrinking,
Thy steps to pursue,
And shield thee, and save thee,
Or perish there too.

—*Thomas Moore*

Roisin Dubh

pour forth in glad - ness on my Roi - sin Dubh.

Had I power, O my loved one, to plead for thy right,
I should boldly speak the truth I know for my heart's own delight.
I should tell to all where'er I go how my deep fondness grew,
And bid them bless the beauty of my Roisin Dubh.

There's no flower that ever bloomed can my sweet rose excel,
There's no tongue that ever moved yet my love can tell.
Had I power, had I skill enough, the world to subdue,
Oh, the queen of all that world so wide should be Roisin Dubh.

Mountain peaks, high and misty, on the moors shall lie low,
And the rushing rivers backward run, the lakes overflow;
The wild breakers of old ocean wear a bright crimson hue,
Ere the world sees the ruin of my Roisin Dubh.

Elegy of Ivor of Keri

What, without your face to cheer it,
Is this weary world to me?
All a place of fogs and shadows,
All a waste without a tree.

Come, beloved, I implore you,
Be my sweetheart, be my wife.
See my heart cast down before you—
Only you can give me life!

The Grey Old Stone

Standing here, thou silent stone, what a world you must have known!
Deeds of glory, lost of story, hast thou witnessed, ancient stone.
Here beneath the grass, tis said, many warrior's bones are laid,
Fighting for their land they fell, none but thou the rest can tell.
Secrets keeping, ever sleeping, dreamst thou of the past, old stone?
—Lyrics by John Oxenford (1914)

French

THE GLORY of French poetry in the Middle Ages was the song of the troubadours and trouvères. They were songmakers for the elite, usually attached to a château, or at least dependent on the patronage of a series of great houses. They sang of love, and their chivalric romances, some of them based upon old legends, were replete with marvelous knightly adventures braved for the sake of one's lady love. The troubadour romances found their way to England where they lasted almost until Chaucer's day, and to Germany where they gave rise to the work of the Minnesingers.

In all three countries the romance was an aristocratic genre which has only an indirect connection with folksong. The jongleurs, who beside juggling could be depended on for general entertainment, seem to have picked up from the troubadours many of their songs and transmitted them to people of their own kind, along with an earthier repertoire. Some of this material inevitably became traditional. But as in Germany, there were two quite independent poetic streams throughout the Middle Ages— one refined and rarefied to please the initiated few, the other unpolished and menial but breathing the folk spirit.

A little pastoral play by Adam de la Halle, called *Le Jeu de Robin et de Marion*, is particularly valuable to us because it contains a number of contemporary popular songs of the thirteenth century. By the time of the Renaissance we hear of Parisian street songs which appealed to the urban equivalent of the peasant class. These "vaux de ville" were in the category of the English broadside ballads, satiric doggerel verses suggested by events of the day and hawked about the poorer quarters.

Most of the old collections of song, though doubtless preserving pieces from a number of centuries, appear today to have been the work of artists, aimed at a general clientele. This is particularly true in the eighteenth century, when an artificial pastoral tradition was fashionable at court. Songs that at first glance appear to be rural turn out to be pure baroque. It is to the modern collections made in the provinces that one must go to see what the people have all the while been singing.

We discover that the traditional song, while it varies considerably from district to district, is remarkably uniform in subject-matter wherever French is spoken. There is the "Noel," simple and beautiful, but occasionally strangely profane; there is the berceuse, the tender lullaby to a gentle tune; there are historical and legendary songs which recall Joan of Arc, the *sans-culottes* or the Biblical Susanna; there are love-songs, which do not anatomize the passion intellectually, but which rather look simply into the heart of the lover and compare his state to familiar natural objects—birds, stars, mountains, streams. And, as we find everywhere, the people have their tavern airs, their soldier and sailor songs, their pieces appropriate to May-day and other festivals, their wedding and funeral chants. Dancing songs are common and the burlesque and satire are not lacking. All over France it is, or has been, possible to duplicate a repertoire of this breadth.

As in Germany the tone lightens the further south one goes. The gaiety of the Midi, expressed in both words and music, contrasts with the more serious and often religious character of the northern songs. Regional differences are most conspicuous near the linguistic frontiers. In Brittany, the Latin and Celtic languages have lived side by side. Haute-Bretagne is characteristically French, but Basse-Bretagne has preserved its Celtic traditions into our own day. Old modal tunes are common (our one example from this region is such a tune), and the rich folksong literature, which has long interested collectors, includes the *gwerz,* or narrative song, and the *sone,* or sentimental dancing-song. Even when the subject-matter has been borrowed, the Breton version is likely to be much altered. Julien Tiersot gives an interesting example of a popular love song called "L'Occasion Manquée," in which a gauche young man fails to make the most of an amorous opportunity and is mocked by three saucy maidens who sing, "When you have an eel, you eat it; . . . when you hold a pretty girl, you kiss her." In the Breton version of this song the coquetry is replaced by the sober praise of female honor, and almost none of the original tone of the French lyric is left.

The Walloons in southern Belgium combine the temper and language of northern France with a virile earthiness which is typically Dutch. Likewise in Alsace, where both French and German are spoken, two cultures are in conflict, with the result that French songs are likely to be heard in either language. In the southeast, French dialects merge imperceptibly into Italian, and most of the dialect songs have a widespread currency from Provence to Piedmont. Although the Pyrenees are a formidable southwestern barrier, the Basque influence has crept into some of the dancing-songs in districts near the Bay of Biscay.

The French are a dancing people, and their dances are of long standing. The bourrée, the branle, the rigaudon, the gavotte are names that found their way into the instrumental suites of the seventeenth and eighteenth centuries. Among the folk these dances assumed rather less elegant proportions than in the concert-hall. Many were accompanied by song, especially the *rondes à danser* of the northern provinces. Purely instrumental dance-tunes were played by bagpipe and hurdy-gurdy. The South has produced a kind of pipe-and-tabor combination in the form of a flute (called the *galoubet*), and a Spanish tambourine beaten with a stick.

The temper of French music, while not as flamboyant as that of Spain or as volatile as that of Italy, is yet never deeply melancholy. There is a kind of dry purity in this music, so that for all its charm it has not the English vigor nor the German heartiness. It is a vehicle for almost unbounded romantic sentiment, yet is itself of classic mold, and of rather mincing feminine daintiness.

Four of the French songs in this volume are from the southern provinces, where they are sung in dialects called *langue d'oc* (distinguished from the northern *langue d'oïl*—"oc" and "oïl," the respective words for "yes," forming a convenient distinction between the two principal linguistic areas of France). "Find Work, My Daughter," a dialogue between mother and daughter on the subject of husbands, is popular throughout the Alpine portions of France and Italy. It has been recorded in the provincial dialects of Provence and Auvergne, Savoy and Piedmont. In *Das Lied der Völker*, Heinrich Möller says that it is sung by wandering young Savoyards, who entertain passersby with a monkey who dances to the tune played on the Jew's harp. "Farandole" is a dancing-song of Dauphiné, also in southeastern France. "Mayday" celebrates the coming of spring and the reawakening of love as symbolized by Mayday. The tune is simple and gay, but contains a surprise in its sudden modulation

from the key of E to G and back again. "Sweet Nightingale" is native to the old province of Béarn in the western Pyrenees. In the eighteenth-century dialect poem by Despourrins, the nightingale makes one of its frequent appearances as a sympathetic spirit to whom the despondent can confide their sorrows. From beyond the mountains the same imagery reappears in the Catalan song "Nightingale."

"Springtime Is Here" is a song of Brittany, the northwestern peninsula inhabited partly by descendants of Celts. The Breton language is not a dialect of French, but is rather related to Welsh and the extinct Cornish. Its literature has been largely imitative except for popular forms such as the ballad and the folk-tale. This spring song has a charming melody in the Dorian mode, with an almost imperceptible modulation six bars from the end. The original folk poem has been replaced by a lyric of François Coppée, the nineteenth-century poet and novelist, whose inspiration was drawn from the humbler strata of society.

"It is May," like "Mayday," was collected in Champagne, and in the song we are to imagine the village priest, accompanied by a procession of young boys and girls, passing through the village streets and soliciting contributions. We possess a large number of so-called begging songs from all over Europe (appropriate to Christmas, New Year's Day or the beginning of spring), in which children ask for dainties or silver in return for wishing good luck to the householders. But the more modern text of this *chanson de quête* promises that the gifts will be put to pious uses.

"Lullaby" is from the island of Corsica. The words are originally in the Italian dialect though they also occur in French patois; the style of the melody is Gallic. A Corsican vendetta song, lamenting the death of a brigand, puts this tune to use for a different purpose.

Find Work, My Daughter

"Well, then, my daughter, choose a steady man."
"Mother, I want a proper gentleman."

"Daughter, a farmer's better than a king."
"Give me a husband who can dance and sing."

"Find one who'll harrow, dig and rake and grub."
"No, no, my mother, we shall keep a pub."

"O my poor daughter, hungry you will be."
"Five sous for white wine, red wine only three."

Dis, ma Jeanette, veux-tu te louer—larirete,
Dis, ma Jeanette, veux-tu te louer?
Non, non, ma mère, je veux me marier—larirete,
Non, non, ma mère, je veux me marier.

Ma pauvre fille, prends un bon garçon—larirete,
Ma pauvre fille, prends un bon garçon.
Plutôt, ma mère, qu'il ait bonn' s façons—larirete,
Plutôt, ma mère, qu'il ait bonn' s façons!

Fais choix d'un homme sachant labourer—larirete,
Fais choix d'un homme sachant labourer.
Je veux qu' aux noces il me fass' danser—larirete,
Je veux qu' aux noces il me fass' danser.

Qu'il pioch' la vigne, et qu'il fan' le foin—larirete,
Qu'il pioch' la vigne, et qu'il fan' le foin.
Non, non, ma mère, nous vendrons du vin—larirete,
Non, non, ma mère, nous vendrons du vin.

Ma pauvre fille, t'auras peu d'argent—larirete,
Ma pauvre fille, t'auras peu d'argent.
Cinq sous du rouge, et trois sous du blanc—larirete,
Cinq sous du rouge, et trois sous du blanc.

Farandole

Straight from the dai — ry, fresh as a fai — ry, Sweet as a
rose the milk maid goes; Sleeps a few hour — s, picks a few
flow — ers, Looks in her glass, and off to Mass. No — thing
more to do to — day! Come to the wed — ding, come to the

wed – ding! No – thing more to do to – day, Dance with the

bride in Dau – phi – né!

Proper young fellows stick to their bellows,
Gentlemen prance and sing and dance;
Drink all day Sunday, sleep all day Monday,
Tuesday come out and walk about.
Nothing more to do today!
Clean out their pipe-bowls, clean out their pipe-bowls!
Nothing more to do today,
Pull on their pipes in Dauphiné!

La bergerette porte florettes,
Des rubans bleus dans les cheveux.
Quand est bien mise part à l'église,
Tout le matin chanter latin.
Tout enfin est terminé—
Faisons la noce,
Faisons la noce,
Tout enfin est terminé,
Faisons la noce en Dauphiné.

Les patriotes portent des bottes,
Les muscadins des souliers fins.
Les jours de fête perdent la tête
Et le lundi sont engourdis.
Puis quand tout est terminé,
Fument leur pipe,
Fument leur pipe,
Puis quand tout est terminé
Fument leur pipe en Dauphiné.

Mayday

Mayday is come, now welcome May.
To our master greetings we bring.
Mayday is come, now welcome May!
Join us, maids, come make a ring.

Mayday is come, now welcome May!
Who'll be first to marry this spring?
Mayday is come, now welcome May!
Join us, maids, come make a ring.

Vétia veni lo zouli ma,
L' alonetta plinta lo ma.
Vétia veni lo zouli ma,
L' alonetta lo plinta.

Vétia veni lo zouli ma,
Noste maistro lo bounsa,
Lo bounsa noste maistro
Nos li saran fédèles.

Vétia veni lo zouli ma,
Lous feilles marirons,
Nous marierons lous feilles puis
Qu'elles sin zoulis.

Springtime Is Here

The fif-ers play, the pip-ers too, Fol-low we all, it is the hour! The wind blows soft, the sky is blue Lan-dou-di-di, lan-dou-di-da Spring-time is here, the or-chards flow-er. The

103

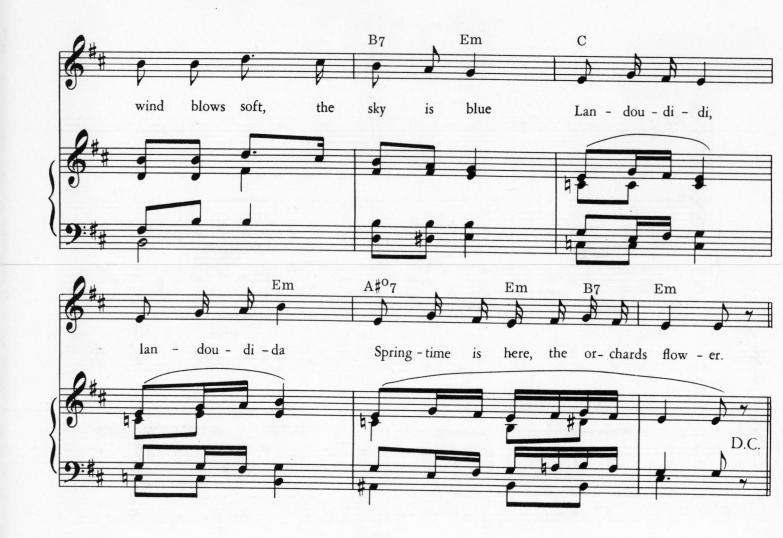

You girls and boys, come form a ring,
Here where the branches make a bower,
Till night comes down we'll dance and sing—
Landoudidi, Landoudida—
Springtime is here, the orchards flower.
Till night comes down we'll dance and sing—
Landoudidi, Landoudida—
Springtime is here, the orchards flower.

Au son du fifre et du biniou,
S'en va gaîment un long cortège.
Le ciel est bleu, le vent est doux—
Landoudidi, landoudida.
Les pommiers ont des fleurs de neige.
Le ciel est bleu, le vent est doux—
Landoudidi, landoudida—
Les pommiers ont des fleurs de neige.

Filles es gars, formez un rond
À l'ombre des feuilles nouvelles,
Et jusqu'au soir nous tournerons—
Landoudidi, landoudida.
Comme les vives hirondelles,
Et jusqu'au soir nous tournerons—
Landoudidi, landoudida—
Comme les vives hirondelles.

It Is May

It is May, lovely May, it's the merry month of May!
When to the field your husband goes,
When to the field your husband goes,
May God him guide and keep from woes,
And He whose death for sin sufficed—Jesus Christ.

It is May, lovely May, it's the merry month of May!
And when you put your child to bed,
And when you put your child to bed,
May God set angels at his head,
And always keep him safe from dread—Praising God.

It is May, lovely May, it's the merry month of May!
Some trifle give us from your shelves,
We shall not use it for ourselves,
But sell it and buy wax to make
A candle for Our Lady's sake—Praising God.

It is May, lovely May, it's the merry month of May!
Good dame, we thank you very much,
And hope we meet with many such.
Within your house we'll pray for you,
And pray when we have left it, too—Praising God.

C'est le mai, le beau mai, c'est le joli mois de mai.
En revenant dedans les champs,
En revenant dedans les champs,
Avons trouvé les blés si grands,
La blanche épine florissant, devant Dieu.

C'est le mai, le beau mai, c'est le joli mois de mai.
Quand vot' mari s'en va dehors,
Quand vot' mari s'en va dehors,
Que Dieu le prenne en son accord,
Et en l'accord de son cher fils, Jésus Christ.

C'est le mai, le beau mai, c'est le joli mois de mai.
Quand vous couchez vot' bel enfant
Quand vous couchez vot' bel enfant
Que Dieu le garde à son coucher,
Et à toute heur' de la journée, devant Dieu.

C'est le mai, le beau mai, c'est le joli mois de mai.
Un petit brin de vot' farin,

C'est pas pour boire ni pour manger,
C'est pour aider avoir un cierg',
Pour y lumer la noble Vierg', devant Dieu.

C'est le mai, le beau mai, c'est le joli mois de mai.
Madam' nous vous remercions,
De vos bonnes intentions,
Nous prions Dieu dans vot' maison,
Aussi quand nous en sortirons, devant Dieu.
C'est le mai, le beau mai, c'est le joli mois de mai.

Lullaby

When you grow to be a lady as one day you will, my blessed,
Mother'll send to town to get you cloth of gold to make you dresses.
  Lullaby, dear, while your mother tells her pretty baby's fortune.

When it's time for you to marry, we shall find a husband for you,
Chief of all our mountain shepherds, he'll be handsome, he'll adore you.
  Lullaby, dear, while your mother tells her pretty baby's fortune.

Oh how proud you'll be, my pretty, when to church, a bride you're going,
Sitting on a horse with trappings, people shouting, bagpipes blowing!
  Lullaby, dear, while your mother tells her pretty baby's fortune.

First will go the handsome bridegroom, wearing boots of finest leather,
After him your happy parents, proudly hand in hand together.
  Lullaby, dear, while your mother tells her pretty baby's fortune.

When the wedding-bells stop ringing, on your horse again we'll seat you,
Then to your new home forever, where his mother waits to greet you!
  Lullaby, dear, while your mother tells her pretty baby's fortune.

Dans les monts de Cuscione la petite a vu le jour.
Et je fais dodelinette pour que dorme mon amour.
La bercait avec tendresse lui prédit sa destinée.

Endors-toi, petite fille, ô bonheur de ta maman.
En beau tissus de laurine je te fais un vêtement.
La bercait avec tendresse lui prédit sa destinée.

Plus tard, tu seras l'épouse du plus brave montagnard,
De celui qui seul commande les bouviers et le chevriers.
La bercait avec tendresse lui prédit sa destinée.

Toute fière, l'epousée passera sur son cheval.
La cornmuse gonflée dans l'escorte s'entendra.
La bercait avec tendresse lui prédit sa destinée.

Ton époux prendra la tête, avec ses cuissards de cuir.
Les parents te feront fête eux si fiers et courageux.
La bercait avec tendresse lui prédit sa destinée.

En arrivant à Mascione où tu dois rester enfin,
Sortira la bellemère qui te touchera la main,
Te donnant, selon l'usage, un grand pot de lait caillé.

Sweet Nightingale

I who must leave the val – ley, I who to ex – ile go, I who must leave my love – ly sweet – heart, Ah, what des – pair I know!

She seemed to know that I must leave her,
Though how, I cannot tell.
Daily I saw her growing paler,
Daily my spirits fell.
When I went out, she'd catch me,
Murmur against my heart,
"Dear, I can never live without you,
Dear, we must never part."

Sweetheart, you know the love I bear you,
Then never doubt my faith.
Nothing shall ever part us, darling,
Yours I will be till death.
If I must leave the valley,
If into exile go,
Whatever woe your heart may suffer,
Mine is an equal woe.

Rossignolet fidèle,
Perché dans le grand bois,
Auprès de ton oiselle,
Tu chant' à pleine voix.
Et moi, pour la montagne,
Le cœur tout endeuillé,
Je quitte ma compagne,
Je pars désespére.

Elle présentait
Le jour du départ—
Mon cœur se mourait—
De la voir souffrir.
D' une voix langoureuse, elle dit,
En me pressant la main:
Que je serais malheureuse—
S'il fallait nous séparer.

Je vous promets, ma chère,
De vous aimer tendrement,
Ma parole est sincère,
Ayez confiance, seulement,
Et soyez assurée que,
Loin de ces jolis yeux,
Si c'était mon destin,
Je souffrirez plus que vous.

Italian

ITALY, FIRST AMONG the nations of Europe to break intellectually with the Middle Ages and establish the spirit of the Renaissance which spread gradually through the West, was almost the last in modern times to recover from the brutal wars of imperialism which early engulfed her. From the time of Columbus' voyages to the rise of Napoleon Italy lay in subjection, cut up into powerless slave states which paid a languid fealty to Austria, Spain and France. The unification of the peninsula was not effected until 1870, just thirteen years before the birth of Mussolini.

In contrast to the turbulent history of recent centuries, Italy's peoples are an extremely happy lot, with all the gaiety and volatile spirits that the temperate Mediterranean latitudes can inspire. This warmth is reflected in the country's folksongs. Italian music is fluid and fluent, whether in the hands of a master or a wayside singer. But the world at large has had to form its opinion of Italian folk music not from the genuine product, which is exceedingly plentiful, but from the deluge of popular art songs typified by "Funiculi, Funicula" and "Santa Lucia." The Neapolitan popular song was a product of a group of industrious and talented city tunesmiths. Its very simple, melodious contours made it easy to assimilate, and whether the songs circulated chiefly in print or by word of mouth, they were quickly caught up and, as it were, consigned to the export trade. But the Neapolitan sentimental ditty with its banal words is not the Italian folksong. Here as in most other countries the traditional lore of the people must be sought in the country, far from the printing press and the song plugger.

Although the narrative ballad is not as important in Italy as in England or Scandinavia, such historical, heroic and legendary pieces are to be found, especially in the northern regions. Perhaps the most popular of all the Italian ballads is one called "Donna Lombarda," which in its poisoning motif resembles the British "Lord Randall." It is current throughout Italy: Barbi collected 116 versions in Sicily alone.

Far more central in Italian folksong is the lyric. In the north the subjects are often French, and the texts are either adapted or bodily translated into the local dialect. Musically the songs of Piedmont and Lombardy are modern in their regularity. Tiersot, who has studied the folk music of the Alps, reports perfectly straightforward major or (occasionally) minor airs, with no trace of the old modes, and with no exotic meters or embellishments. In Venice the songs of the gondoliers are now those that would please an urban clientele, but it was not always thus. Even a century ago they sang traditional *barcarolles,* and Wagner records ecstatically how on a sleepless night he wandered to his balcony for a breath of air, and from the Grand Canal heard a gondolier singing a famous old song with words from Tasso's *Jerusalem Delivered.* Mendelssohn wrote three Venetian boat-songs based upon familiar rhythmical patterns (usually a slow, dreamy 6/8) and melodic phrases of the *gondolieri.*

Further south two kinds of song are commonly found. The *stornello,* which abounds in Tuscany and Sicily, is composed usually of three-line stanzas. The first line introduces the name of a flower, with which the third line must rhyme. Singers often improvised them. Browning quotes (or improvises) several in *Fra Lippo Lippi:*

> *Flower o' the broom,*
> *Take away love,*
> *And our earth is a tomb!*
> *Flower o' the quince,*
> *I let Lisa go,*
> *And what good in life since?*

These concentrated bits of song recall the same epigrammatic tendency to be found in the Spanish *copla* and the Greek distich. The Latvian *daina* is the same sort of folksong in four lines.

The second variety of structure is that of the *rispetti* (Sicilian *canzuni*), which has a stanza of eight lines. It is used for serenades and aubades, some of which are common to all the Italian provinces. Several of the songs in this section are of the *rispetto* type.

Folksongs are usually sung in unison, but in Italy a second part is sometimes added, in thirds below the melody. This is probably not a folk inspiration, but is to be ascribed rather to an imitation of popular composers. The harmonic basis of most of the nation's folksongs is simple; the underlying tonic and dominant chord structure may owe something to the widespread popularity of the guitar and the mandolin. In southern districts there still remain noticeable traces of the old Spanish-Moorish character in the dance rhythms and the Oriental details of some scales. The mordants, turns and other embellishments may be Spanish, but with equal likelihood they may derive from the ornamentation common in coloratura singing.

The dancing tunes were often accompanied by song. The commonest types are the internationally known *tarantella* and the leaping *saltarello,* both of which are illustrated among the songs in this volume. They are extremely vigorous dances in triple time, and are chiefly popular in the south. In Venice there is a kind of whirling gigue in 6/8 known as the *furlana.* Instrumental dance tunes were played by a variety of instruments, including the *piffero* or bagpipe, which can yet be found in Sicily and the Abruzzi. The *piffero* requires two players, one of whom has the bag with the drones, the other the chanter. Groups of *pifferari* are still reported to descend from the hills of the Abruzzi to Naples at Christmas time to perform in the streets. One of their pieces seems to have been the source of the "Pastoral Symphony" in Handel's *Messiah.*

Although the impress of folksong on art music has been relatively slight, the influence in the opposite direction has, as one writer put it, "almost swamped folk music." The Italian opera composers whose forte was smoothly-flowing sentimental melody have long since been forgotten, but the temporary popularity of their work created a public taste which was not thereafter satisfied by the folk tune alone. From the eighteenth century to the present the folksong and the popular song have existed side by side with little advantage to the former, and, as has already been suggested, the Neapolitan school has made itself conspicuous with melodic gems of a superficial sort, coupled with words perhaps less meritorious than the average product of America's Tin Pan Alley.

The music of Sicily is perhaps the most interesting to be found in any section of Italy. The stamp of all the conquerors has left it more varied than that of other districts, and though the island is small, a single collector has gathered more than five thousand Sicilian songs. Other regions with marked individuality include some parts of Calabria, where the Greek inhabitants have their own songs, and the Tyrol, into which the Austrian influence has penetrated. The essential Italian idiom is well-formed, simple melody with plenty of emotional coloring, and that is everywhere present.

The Italian songs in our collection are relatively modern provincial pieces. "Mother, the Bells Are Ringing" and "Before I Had Found a Sweetheart" come from the central Abruzzi hills. "All Beauty Within You," from the Romagna in the east, is, like most of the others, a love-song. As Marzo suggests, it is popular and traditional, but does not present the characteristics of a folksong. "Lullaby" is an example of the *ninnananna,* as the Italians call the process of rocking a baby to sleep while singing to it. The tune seems to be a kind of improvisation on half a dozen notes, and produces a strangely somnolent effect.

The remainder of the songs are from southern Italy and Sicily. "The Shark" is a Neapolitan tarantella, on the singular subject of a shark frightening bathers. The tarantella is a fast 6/8 dance, always in minor. Its name is said to be derived from the belief that a person

bitten by a tarantula can purge himself of the poison by dancing violently enough to exude perspiration freely. It seems clear that this is a popular superstition, but tarantism was a genuine enough type of dance-madness, whether excited by the bite of a harmless spider or not. Percy Scholes in his *Oxford Companion to Music* wryly suggests that "In the nineteenth century, whilst these occasional outbreaks of tarantism still occurred and the traditional remedy was applied, musicians made more money out of tarantellas by their merits as compositions than by their merits as therapeutic agents." "Saltarella" is a kind of tarantella with jumps, in which the rhythm is based on a quarter-note followed by an eighth, instead of running triplets.

"Neapolitan Fisher's Song" is a Neapolitan love song whose beautiful melody, while clearly sentimental, would scarcely call for the present extravagant text were this not Italian. For us there is more unconscious humor than grimness in the idea of the lover returning from Hell to teach his heartless inamorata what Hell is really like. Many American songs of the 'nineties trafficked in the same sort of sobby sentimentalism.

"La Sicillitana" is by G. L. Cottrau (1797-1847), the composer of "Santa Lucia" and many other Neapolitan songs popular in their time. The bolero rhythm and the chromatics show the Moorish influences on the Neapolitan style, to be accounted for by the onetime Spanish occupation of the region. Although the air may have been adapted from an actual folk melody, it is most probable that we have here the common phenomenon of an art-song cast in a consciously popular vein. The same may be said of the Sicilian "When I Raise My Eyes," and both poems would appear to be the hackwork of a poetaster. Dr. Deutsch has observed, however, that "of the melodies, even the best song composer may be jealous."

Mother, the Bells Are Ringing

Mother, mother, if I should tell you
How hard I pray, you would not believe me!
Mother, mother, if I should tell you
How hard I pray, you would not believe me!

All day long I am praying, praying,
"Please never let my beloved leave me!"
All day long I am praying, praying,
"Please never let my beloved leave me!"

Mamma, mamma, lasciami andare
Là nella chiesa del buon Signore,
Mamma, mamma, lasciami andare
Là nella chiesa del buon Signore,
Colla bocca potrò pregare
Mentre cogli occhi farò l'amore.
Colla bocca potrò pregare
Mentre cogli occhi farò l'amore.

Mamma, mamma, fo la preghiera.
Tu non lo credi, con tanto ardore,
Mamma, mamma, fo la preghiera
Tu non lo credi, con tanto ardore,
Prego il cielo mattina e sera
Che dell' amante mi serbi il core.
Prego il cielo mattina e sera
Che dell' amante mi serbi il core.

Before I Had Found a Sweetheart

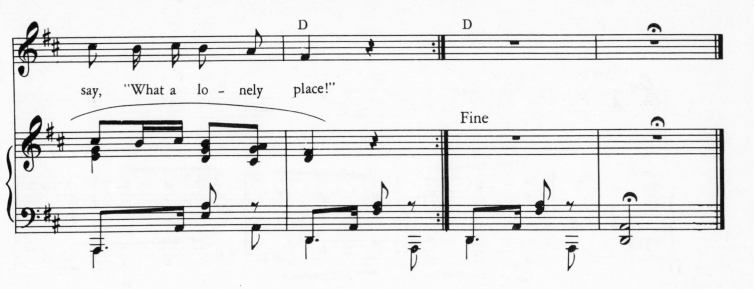

say, "What a lo - nely place!"

Fine

I live in the same small cottage,
But, oh, what a change inside it!
I found me a girl to marry,
My heart has a heart beside it.
The sun, when he sees our cottage,
Shines out at his very fairest;
The sun, looking in our window,
Calls down, "What a happy pair!"

Tenevo una casetta,
Con una finestretta aperta,
La luna, facendovi capolino,
Diceva: Non c'è nessuno!
Ma ora non è più così;
Questo cuore ha trovato un cuore,
Il sole ci guarda, e ride
Dicendo: Beati voi!

All Beauty Within You

All beau — ty with — in you, all gra — ces a — round you, So

late — ly I found you, so soon we must part! Ah,

no, no, no, weep not, take cour — age, my beau — ty, To

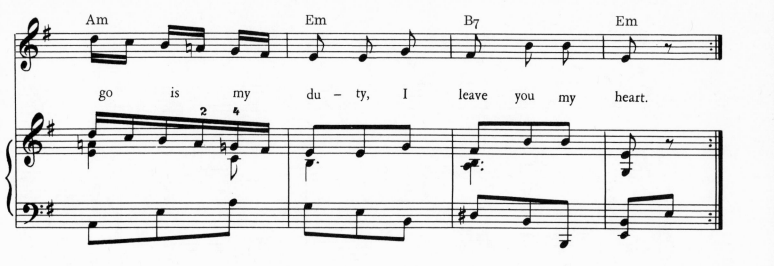

go   is   my   du – ty,   I   leave   you   my   heart.

All day of you thinking, all night of you dreaming,
My life is but seeming when we are apart.
Ah, no, no, no, weep not, take courage, my beauty,
To go is my duty, I leave you my heart.

I swear to return you the life you have lent me.
No force shall prevent me, not Death with his dart.
Ah, no, no, no, weep not, take courage, my beauty,
To go is my duty, I leave you my heart.

Sei bella negli occhi, sei bella nel core,
Sei tutta un amore, se nata per me.
Ah, no, no, no, non pianger, coraggió, ben mio,
Quest'ultimo addio ricevi da me.

Ti vedo se veglio, se dormo ti vedo,
E viver non credo diviso da te.
Ah, no, no, no, non pianger, coraggió, ben mio,
Quest'ultimo addio ricevi da me.

Sei bella nel viso, nel pianto sei bella,
E barbara stella mi parte da te.
Ah, no, no, no, non pianger, coraggió, ben mio,
Quest'ultimo addio ricevi da me.

Ma s'io da te parto, qui resto coll'alma,
Tu gioja, tu calma, sei solo per me.
Ah, no, no, no, non pianger, coraggió, ben mio,
Quest'ultimo addio ricevi da me.

Sei bella, e vagando su rive straniere
Sarò col pensiere io sempre con te.
Ah, no, no, no, non pianger, coraggió, ben mio,
Quest'ultimo addio ricevi da me.

Tu pensa che fede ti do in questo giorno
Che s'io non ritorno son morto per te.
Ah, no, no, no, non pianger, coraggió, ben mio,
Quest'ultimo addio ricevi da me.

Lullaby

Queen of Heav'n, Our Blessed Lady,
Watch beside my sleeping baby,
Watch beside my sleeping baby,
Queen of Heav'n, Our Blessed Lady.
By-bye, sleep now, my baby,
By-bye, my baby, go to sleep, my baby,
Go to sleep, my pretty baby.

You who watched beside the Manger,
Guard my sleeping child from danger,
Guard my sleeping child from danger,
You who watched beside the Manger.
By-bye, sleep now, my baby,
By-bye, my baby, go to sleep, my baby,
Go to sleep, my pretty baby.

Fa la nina nina nana,
Mi bambino dormirà
Mi bambino dormirà
Fa la nina nina nana!
Nana la nina nana.
La nina nana, fa la nina nana;
Mio bambino dormirà.

La Madonna di Loreto
Che ti vien a star al letto,
Che ti vien a star al letto!
La Madonna di Loreto.
Nana la nina nana.
La nina nana, fa la nina nana;
Mio bambino dormirà.

La Madonna della Guardia
Che ti guardi, Che ti salvi,
Che ti guardi, che ti salvi!
La Madonna della Guardia!
Nana la nina nana.
La nina nana, fa la nina nana;
Mio bambino dormirà.

Saltarella

All - to - geth - er, dance to - geth - er, Moth- ers and maids, come dance to -

geth - er! Round the ends and down the mid - dle! Quick or I'll put up my

fid - dle! All - to - fid - dle! Ha, ha, ha! What a

E abballàti, e abballàti, fimmini schetti e maritati,
E s'un abballati bonu, nun vi cantu e nun vi sonu.
E abballàti, e abballàti, fimmini schetti e maritati,
E s'un abballàti bonu, nun vi cantu e nun vi sonu.
Sciu, sciu, sciu! Quantu fimmini chici su'!

Ci nn'e quattru scafazzati, i facemu cu' i patati!
Ci n'e quattru ammaccateddi, i facemu cu' i piseddi!
Sciu, sciu, sciu! Quantu fimmini chici su'!
Ci nn'e quattru scafazzati, i facemu cu' i patati!
Ci n'e quattru ammaccateddi, i facemu cu' i piseddi!

The Shark (Tarantella)

Oh, how often I have strolled there,
Watched the girl that I adore,
Swimming, diving, splashing water,
Running races down the shore!

Why, O mighty ocean monster,
Why our humble coast explore?
Devil take your explorations!
To the sea she goes no more.
Devil take your explorations!
To the sea she goes no more.

Là nel mare ogni mattina
Io vedea la bimba mia,
Di tant'altre in compagnia
La vedevo agnor colà.
Alle cose le più strane
Oggi fede ognor si dà?
È venuto il pesce cane,
Ella ai bagni più non va.
È venuto il pesce cane,
Ella ai bagni più non va.

Quante volte io la vedevo
La mia bimba grassa e tonda
Folleggiar, scherzar con l'onda,
Correr qua, venir di là.
Perchè venne proprio qua?
Perchè venne proprio qua?
Maledetto il pesce cane,
Ella a'bagni più non va.
Maledetto il pesce cane,
Ella a'bagni più non va.

When I Raise My Eyes

When the doctor came, he watched me,
Saw my pain in every feature.
Then I set myself to tell him
How you torture me, proud creature.
When he heard me, thus he answered:
"Boy, this passion no more cherish!
If you will not leave this woman—
Thus I warn you—you surely will perish."

When I heard the doctor speaking,
Thus I answered, loudly crying,
"I will never leave my sweetheart,
I am not afraid of dying.
Ask her, ask her,—she will tell you,
Hers I'll be, whate'er befall me.
Death I welcome! Hers I'll perish!
Men a martyr, no traitor, shall call me!"

When I heard the doctor speaking,
Thus I answered, loudly crying,
"I will never leave my sweetheart,
I am not afraid of dying.
Ask her, ask her,—she will tell you,
Hers I'll be, whate'er befall me.
Death I welcome! Hers I'll perish!
Men a martyr, no traitor, shall call me!"

Te guardando spesso spesso
Io mi sento disturbato
Nè'l mio sangue è più lo stesso
Como un gel proprio s'è fatto.
Io ti guardo con questi occhi,
Muoio spasimo e deliro,
E mi sento dentro al core,
Mancamenti di respiro.

Venne 'l medico a osservare
I mie 'affanni e le mie pene,
Io gli misi a raccontare
La cagione d'onde viene.
Ed il medico mi disse:
Figlio, lascia sta partita,
Se tal donna tu non lasci,
Poco dura la tua vita.

Io sentendo quel parlare,
Gli risposi a voce forte:
Nè la donna io so lasciare,
Nè timore ho della morte.
Ella stessa lo può dire
S'è sincero questo amore;
Di morir io son contento,
Non chiamarmi traditore!

Neapolitan Fisher's Song

132

Hear - ing my oar - locks creak - ing, when in my boat I row ah! I seem to hear you speak - ing, hear you still say - ing "No!"

I hear my mother crying softly beneath her breath.
She sees her son is dying—will she not pray for death?
No hope have I to win you; pity, my only plea!—ah!—
Have you a heart within you? Then pity her and me!

If still you feel no pity—when I am buried deep,
I'll break from death's black city, haunt you, destroy your sleep.
No more will I beseech you, grimly beside you dwell!—ah!—
I'll come from Hell to teach you what are the pains of Hell!

Perchè si cruda sei? mi fai morir perchè?
La vita io ti darei: tu dai la morte a me.
Se vo pescando in mare, se afflitto in terra sto, ah!
Veder sempre mi pare che tu mi dica no—var!

Siccome can mi caccia, speranza non mi dà!
Deh! tu mi guarda in faccia, un tisico son già.
Il remo io più non reggo non tiro rete io più . . .
Mercè sempre ti chieggo, ma scoglio ognor sei tu!

La vecchia madre plora vedendo il mio dolor.
Se avvien che il figlio mora, morrà la madre ancor!
Io non ti cerco amore, pietà vogl'io da te!
Se tu rinserri in core, pietà di lei, di me!

Ma se tu cor non hai, se tu mi fai morir,
Qual ombra mi vedrai ne'sonni tuoi venir.
Con strazii e con terrori pentire io ti vo'far.
E prima che tu muori l'inferno hai da provar!

La Scillitana (The Girl from Scilla)

Deep in the dark-some for-est, I saw a ti - ger, I saw a ti - ger who sought for prey.

Water, on marble falling, on marble falling,
On marble falling, day after day,
Softens the hardest marble, as well it may,
As well it may, as well it may.

Yet you, hard-hearted creature, so full of beauty,
So full of beauty, so wholly fair,
Hearing my better weeping, you do not care,
You do not care, you do not care.

Vitti na tigra dinta
Na silva 'scura, na silva 'scura,
E cu lu chiantu miu,
Mansueta far ri, mansueta far ri.

Vitti cu l'acqua na
Marmura dura, marmura dura,
Calannu a guccia, a guccia,
Arrimuddari, arrimuddari!

E vui che siti bedda
Criatura, criatura, criatura.
Vi ni riditi di stu
Chiantu amari, chiantu amari!

136

Spanish

THE SPANISH PENINSULA, like Greece and the Balkans, has been subject to foreign musical influences in her impressionable past. Where the eastern countries were occupied by Turks, Spain was overrun by the Moors; but in both cases the presence of an Oriental musical tradition alongside the Occidental has made profound differences in the nature of the national idiom. Ironically enough, the national idiom is much more readily discernible to us at a distance than it would be if we were to travel throughout Spain in search of it. For the distinctive rhythms of *jota*, *seguidilla* and *bolero* mean Spain to us; but in the land itself we should discover at once that regional differences are of such great importance that, as in our own folk music, we should be fearful of trying to define simply and in general terms just what the distinctive features of Spanish music are.

One thing is certain, however. The guitar is the national instrument, and we have in Spain an almost unique phenomenon in folk music: voice and guitar make a single entity; that is, melody and accompaniment are inseparable, giving the song a harmonic basis rare in folk music. Whereas in most countries the song is but the melodic line itself (and any harmonic patterns superimposed on it are likely to be mere artificial additions), in Spanish song and dance the guitar establishes unquestionably a set of harmonies—basically tonic and dominant —around which the melody revolves. And the instrumental accompaniment supplies a strong rhythm, often subtle and detailed in the extreme. Perhaps the only comparable situation is to be found in the songs of the old Irish and Welsh harpers. But the differences in temperament are at once apparent.

If the guitar unites Spain into a single musical region, we have but to look closer to see the important subdivisions, which owe their individual differences to a complex of geographical, historical and racial forces. The Catalonian regions to the northeast seem but a continuation of the French Midi. As Julien Tiersot has pointed out, Catalan music has much less relationship to that of the other regions of Spain than to the French beyond the Pyrenees. Their songs exploit similar subjects, 6/8 time is popular, and the lyrics are built from small couplets, often with internal rhymes. The Basque districts, lying also in the north of Spain, partake of the qualities of both nations, but have tenaciously preserved the archaisms of the ecclesiastical modal scales. As we proceed southward into Andalusia, we note the increasing presence of Oriental scales, and the deepening impress of Moorish culture. Andalusian music is the basis for most foreign knowledge of Spanish song and dance, but George Chase in his admirable book *The Music of Spain* (New York, 1941) is careful to point out that almost

unknown to outsiders is the characteristically melancholy *canto jondo,* or deep song. The interior districts are less affected by foreign infiltration, and in La Mancha and the Madrid regions one may feel that "pure" Spanish characteristics prevail. Most striking of all, perhaps, is the northwestern district of Galicia, near the Portuguese border, where the old Celtic occupation has left its mark. The Celtic melancholy, expressed in songs more stolid rhythmically than in other Spanish districts, extends over into Portugal, but seems to be an unnaturalized Iberian quality. Here only does the guitar yield supremacy to a native variety of the bagpipe.

Spanish folksong, as it lives today with astonishing vitality, is not remarkably ancient. But the old *romancero,* which began to find its way into print in the sixteenth century, forms a link with the western European ballads and chivalric romances of the late Middle Ages. Narrative has long since given place to lyric, however; Spain has its occupational and its festival songs, yet the predominant subject of the modern folksong is love. It is commonly found that narrative songs tend to exist largely for their story, lyric poems rather for the beauty of their music, or at least with far greater consciousness of the song *as* music. With the lyric, the melodic line is ordinarily more richly developed than in the improvisational chants to which heroic poems are sung. If this generalization be true for other countries, it is unusually applicable to Spain. There, if anything, the words themselves have been subordinated to the music. The bulk of the volatile emotion of the folksong is conveyed by the melody and the voice. The actual texts are often slight, and seldom reach any greater depth of expression than is found in the "conceits" of the extravagant Elizabethan sonneteers in England. If one concentrates enough on the abstract emotion of love, he can occupy himself with his mistress' eyebrow or the dimple in her cheek. And it is in that spirit that many of the Spanish *coplas,* or couplets, are conceived. The music, then, is dominant.

Moreover, the song is never far removed from the dance. The rhythms of the guitar are supremely "danceable," and one is not surprised to find that the Andalusian *cante flamenco* of Gypsy origin is often danced, giving rise to many characteristic regional dances, such as the *granadinas,* the *malagueña,* the *sevillanas,* that take their names from cities. Similarly, the *jota,* the *seguidilla,* the *fandango,* though primarily dances, are frequently interpolated or accompanied with song.

The great variety of Spanish music has not been evident in its exported product. Indeed, it may be said with some justice that Spain has kept the best for her own consumption and has sent abroad the trinkets and glass beads which will catch the eye and ear of the novelty-seeking foreigners. Thus the Spanish-American idioms have not always profited by the best of the mother country's resources.

Some rich aspects of Spanish music may be inadequately represented in the present collection, for two reasons. First, the influence of the Arabian Moors, of the Sephardic Jews, of the Gypsies, and of the Gregorian plainsong has all led toward the exotic, that is to say, the irregular and complex. Many folksongs contain elaborate embroidery of the melodic line difficult for the unpracticed singer to execute, and microtones are impossible to record except in Byzantine notation. The bizarre pieces are interesting, but, as with much of the older Hungarian song, they are so far from being primitive that because of their very subtlety they cannot profitably find place in a popular collection. Secondly, much of the modern folksong, regular in rhythm and simple melodically, is musically shallow.

Spanish folk music at its best is inimitable, as a Granados and a De Falla have shown us; and Spain's best folksong is, for the present,

easier to enjoy than to perform.

"Seguidilla from La Mancha" is dance music from La Mancha, the home of the fabulous Don Quixote. In this district southeast of Madrid the *seguidilla* is alternately sung and played as accompaniment to the dance. The music, with its swift interplay of major and minor and its vigorous syncopation, is in an idiom familiar to the western hemisphere. The words are vivacious, and combine native pride in Manzanares, "where life is gay and free," with an appropriate sentiment for the only girl in this peerless town.

"Harvesting" is a rural dancing song in which the alternation of voice and guitar separates the lines of the bucolic love poem. The music is itself made up of small melodic ideas, and the typical quick "turn" adds a pungent rhythm to the five-measure phrases and the irregular meter of the *coplas.*

"Nightingale" is a Catalan song with French provincial characteristics which begin with the opening word of the song. Here, as in "Sweet Nightingale" from southern France, the lover sings his troubles to the nightingale. The music, too, is closer to the style of the Mediterranean provinces of France and northern Italy than to the Andalusian. The melodic line is smooth and unsyncopated; the rhythm is that of the *chanson* rather than the *cante.*

"The Violet" is a song from the Basque country in northern Spain. In an area about twice the size of Rhode Island, near Bilbao on the Bay of Biscay, live the people who speak a language unrelated to any other European tongue. In folkways they have preserved the primitive, which partake of both Spanish and French characteristics, but their dances are highly individualized, and they delight in 5/4 time (popular also in Finland). Here we have a native lyric with French delicacy of feeling. Unlike similar songs from northern countries, no symbolism need be read into the poem to make it complete.

Seguidilla from La Mancha

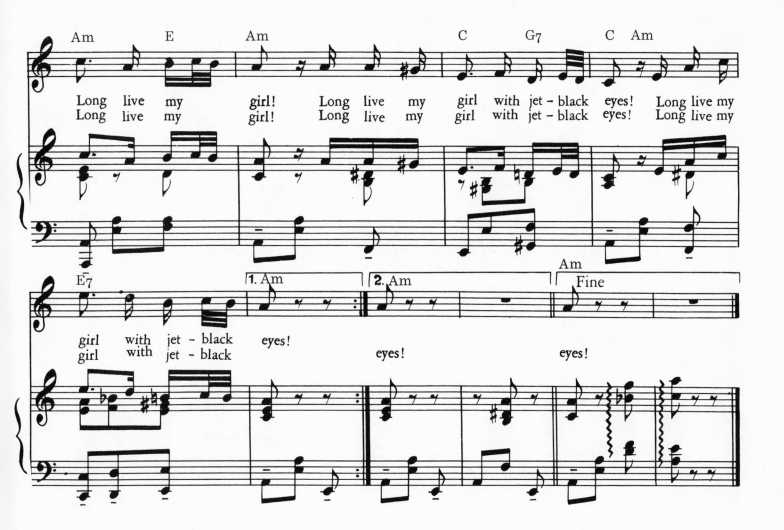

La Mancha's songs are gay as spring,
The only songs I sing!
They're neat songs, they're sweet songs—
Long I've known them, long may I sing them!
Long may their echoes ring!
Long live La Mancha! etc.

Your eyes, girl, dart now fire, now snow.
They're fire when they glow,
When your love, when your love
Comes to meet you, when his eyes greet you.
For all the rest, they're snow!
Long live La Mancha! etc.

Aunque la Mancha tenga dos mil lugares
no hay otro más salado
que Manzanares,
no hay otro más salado
que Manzanares.

!Viva la Mancha!
!Vivan los ojos negras
de mi muchacha,
de mi muchacha!

Seguidillas manchegas cantar yo quiero
por que son las que tienen
sal y salero,
por que son las que tienen
sal y salero.

!Viva la Mancha!
y vivan sus cantares
con sal y gracia,
con sal y gracia!

Fuego y nieve despiden, niña, tus ojos:
fuego para quien amas,
nieve a los otros.
Y yo te ruego que aunque
me hagas cenizas me arrojen fuego.

!Viva la Mancha! etc.

Cuatro lunares tienes, niña, en tu rostro:
tienes abril y mayo,
julio y agosto.
De tal manera tienes, niña,
en tu cara la primavera.

!Viva la Mancha! etc.

Nada me aflige y tengo melancolía;
yo no sé de qué nace
la pena mia.
Solo me alivio cada vez
que me miras y yo te miro.

!Viva la Mancha! etc.

Harvesting

mong green leaves. Four pine-trees, four

pine-trees, so strong, so tall, They are

all that you own—you, more sweet than crim-son cher-ries A-

mong green leaves. And I guard them, I

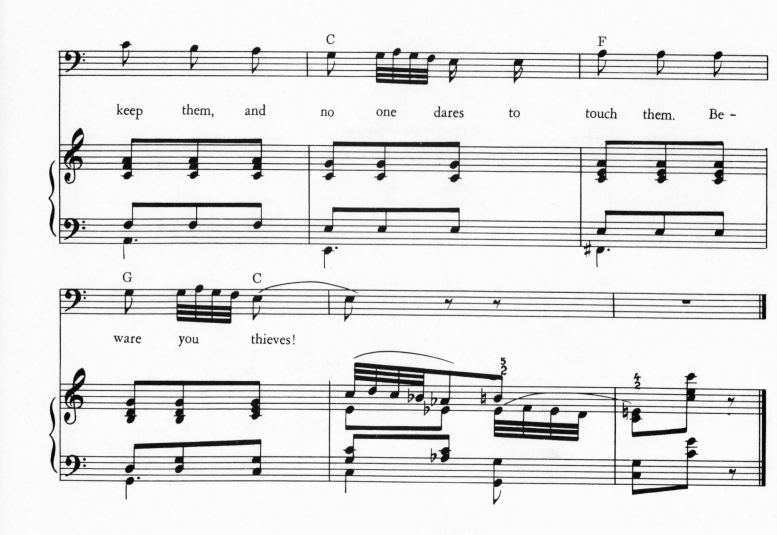

keep them, and no one dares to touch them. Be-

ware you thieves!

Segaba ya aquella tarde,
Ỳ ella atropaba la yerba,
Y estaba más colorada, morena y salada
Que en su sazon las cerezas.
Cuatro pinos tiene tu pinar y yo te los cuido,
Cuatro majos los quieren cortar, no se han atrevido.

Nightingale

man · he made me mar – ry, Loun – ges while I fetch and car – ry. Night-ing –

ale so strong – ly fly – ing, don't fail. _____

I have lost my good bell-wether, nightingale,
But the cowherd caught him for me,
Nightingale so strongly flying, nightingale, don't fail.

Cowherd, give me my bell-wether, nightingale.
"If I do, what will you give me?"
Nightingale so strongly flying, nightingale don't fail.

Come and kiss me—that I'll give you, nightingale.
One, I say, just one, not twenty,
Stop it, stop it, that is plenty!
Nightingale so strongly flying, don't fail.

Rossinyol que vas a França, rossinyol,
Encomana'm a ma mare, rossinyol
D'un bel bocatge, rossinyol, d'un vol.

Encomana'm a ma mare, rossinyol,
I a mon pare no pas gaire, rossinyol,
D'un bel bocatge, rossinyol d'un vol.

I a mon pare no pas gaire, rossinyol,
Perquè a un pastor m'ha dado
Que m' fa guardar la remada,
Rossinyol d'un bel bocatge, d'un vol.

He perduda l'esquellada, rossinyol,
Lo vaquer me l'ha atrapada, rossinyol,
d'un bel bocatge, rossinyol, d'un vol.

Vaquer, torna me'n la cabra, rossinyol,
¿Què m'en donaras per paga? rossinyol,
D'un bel bocatge, rossinyol d'un vol.

Un petò i una abraçada, rossinyol,
Això sòn coses de mainatge,
Quan tenen pa, volen formatge,
Rossinyol d'un bel bocatge, d'un vol.

The Violet

148

Sweet - ness of scent re-veals you, tells me your hid – ing- place.

D.C.

Violet, other flowers dance all the livelong day,
Dance to the happy music breezes, like fiddlers, play.
You, under grass half hidden, seem not to hear the sound,
Stand like a humble widow, staring upon the ground.
You, under grass half hidden, seem not to hear the sound,
Stand like a humble widow, staring upon the ground.

Violet, all the flowers call you to dance with them,
Ask you to spread your petals, ask you to raise your stem.
Fear not! All flowers love you. Violet, show your face.
See where the rose is standing? That is your proper place.
Fear not! All flowers love you. Violet, show your face.
See where the rose is standing? That is your proper place.

Alferretan haiz sortzen, oi lore maitea,
Baratze bazterretan, humilki gordea.
Bafada goxoenak hau bethi salatzen:
Hir' egoitza bakotxak errexki kausitzen.
Bafada goxoenak hau bethi salatzen:
Hir' egoitza bakotxak errexki kausitzen.

Oi erradak zertako haizen hoin herabe?
Eder duk modestia, bainan gaindi gabe.
Berthutean orobat, bertzetan bezala,
Jakizak, ez badakik, negurri badela.
Berthutean orobat, bertzetan bezala,
Jakizak, ez badakik, negurri badela.

Bertze lore guziak, sorthu bezam sarri,
Arrai, dantzan bizi tuk, zefir soinulari:
Hi aldiz belharpean, burua behera,
Alhargun bat iduri, lurrari begira.
Hi aldiz belharpean, burua behera,
Alhargun bat iduri, lurrari begira.

Hire lagunek haute beren gana deitzen,
Zeren hauten guziek bihotzez maitatzen.
Altxa beraz lurretik, ez ukh' ethorkia!
Arrosaren aldean duk hire tokia.
Altxa beraz lurretik, ez ukh' ethorkia!
Arrosaren aldean duk hire tokia.

149

Finnish

FINLAND, THE "LAND of a thousand lakes," was one of the many independent nations created at the end of the First World War. She had been a Grand Duchy under Russian control for more than a century, and before that had been the fighting ground of Russia and Sweden, belonging now to one, now to the other, occasionally divided between them. Although in the nineteenth century the Finns enjoyed somewhat more autonomy than their southern neighbors across the Baltic Sea, the Russian efforts to domesticate the Grand Duchy were exactly like the steps taken all over the Empire to quench any sparks of national or racial ambition.

The Finns[1] were separated by a wide lin-

[1] The Esthonians are closely related linguistically to the Finns; geographically and historically they are to be grouped with Latvia and Lithuania. The records of Esthonian folk-song are meager and their music is therefore not considered in this discussion.

guistic barrier from all the surrounding peoples. Finnish, like Basque and Hungarian, does not belong to the Indo-European family of languages, which includes almost every other tongue spoken on the continent. Finnish and Hungarian are the most important members of the so-called Finno-Ugrian group, but, as one authority puts it, they are about as alike as English and Persian. Finnish is incredibly complex—the noun, for example, has fifteen cases where English has three—and, as with the Hungarians, the language has proved an important factor in preserving cultural identity in the face of repression.

Valuable also has been the large body of Finnish epic poetry and the almost universal love of song among the natives. Contemporaneous with the Russian literary revival led by Pushkin, Dr. Elias Lönnrot, a Finnish physician, traveled throughout his country, recording all sorts of folk poetry from the lips of singers. He first published a rather miscellaneous volume in which he made no attempt to separate lyric, magic and epic songs. But he soon discovered that the epic songs had a basic unity, and he redoubled his collecting efforts. Once he had gathered all he could find, he set about the delicate business of joining them into a continuous story. In 1835 he published his work as the *Kalevala,* which has been known since as the Finnish national epic. Actually, it is not an epic in the usual sense, since it was pieced together out of minor songs which existed independently of the whole saga. But it is a masterful expression of the Finnish national spirit, and is thought of today on a par with the *Beowulf* and the *Song of Roland.* Longfellow imitated its highly individual meter (from a German translation) in *The Song of Hiawatha,* and echoed incidentally no little of the strange and haunting spirit of the Finnish original.

The individual songs out of which the *Kalevala* was fashioned belong to a class of folk poetry known as the *runo.*[1] They are sung by two men who sit facing each other on a rock, their fingers interlocked. As the leader begins to sing, they sway back and forth to the rhythm of the chant. Before he has finished the first line the second singer joins him in singing the end of the line, and then repeats the whole line alone. They are accompanied by a third man who sits at a little distance playing the *kantele,* a kind of zither which has been the national instrument for an estimated two thousand years. Each *runo* has its own rather monotonous traditional melody, ordinarily in 5/4 time, which is repeated for every line with slight variation.

---

[1] Even older are the laments known as *joiku,* sung to brief recitative melodies. Historically they are of some importance, as remnants of this Finnish type have been found also among the Laplanders.

Lönnrot's vast collections included old magic songs and lyrics called *kanteletar,* some of which he wove into the *Kalevala.* More important for our immediate purpose are the modern types of folksong called *laulu,* at once highly melodious and very influential on contemporary composers. The Finnish idiom as it is known to the artistic world today has to a remarkable degree been founded on folk music. Ever since Robert Kajanus' successful *Finnish Rhapsody* (1882) the native composers have, like the nationalist Russians, sought their inspiration in indigenous materials, and the result has given an intense stimulation to Finland's musical life. It happens that Sibelius did not use folk melodies in his symphonic works, yet he had become so imbued with a national musical idiom based on folk music that as a consequence his themes seem to "express the race."

There are several musical dialects in Finland. The coastal regions, as in Greece, have felt the force of western influence, here Swedish and Scandinavian generally. In the east the Slavic coloring is visible, while in the interior where only Finnish is spoken and there is not much traffic with the outside world, the native idiom is untroubled by alien conventions. In no country is music more vital to the ordinary life of a people. The Finns have as large a body of folksong as is to be found anywhere. Much of the singing is in choruses, and on a more consciously artistic level Finnish male choirs have become famous all over Europe.

Both secular and sacred songs are of a popular character, and there is a large body of dance music, much of it indebted to Continental models such as the quadrille and reel, and more boisterous types such as the polka. Musically the melodies are firm in texture, with some primitive elements still visible in the numerous modal tunes. A large proportion of the songs express sadness, grief or doubt, but genuine uncorrupted examples are never sentimental. The emotion is full-bodied but masculine, frank yet not treacly. There is gaiety, too, especially in the songs of the eastern or Karelian districts and in the southern islands. But whenever Finnish music is to be heard, it is impressive in its vigor, its clean earthiness, its fine freshness of melodic ingenuity.

The eight Finnish folksongs divide themselves naturally into three groups. They all represent the modern, as distinct from the *runo* style, and most of them reveal foreign influences at work. "All Alone," "Come Back to Me," "The Rosebush" and "At the Cherry Tree" are typical western Finnish songs, with Swedish flavoring. "Come Back to Me" has been used as thematic material in a splendid anthem by F. Melius Christiansen, "Lost in the Night." "We've Had a Dance" is a polka—a Finnish polka, to be sure, revealing the assimilation of modern dance forms into the native idiom. "The Rosebush," "Rallialei" and "The Birch Tree" are typically Baltic. Here the Finnish character asserts itself without contamination. Two of the three are modal tunes ("Rallialei" is Aeolian, "The Birch Tree" is Dorian). All of the group are musically interesting; their lyric contour is simple, but the harmonic pattern is not stereotyped as in, say, the German and Czech dance tunes, or the average American folk tune with which we are familiar.

Rallialei

Father and mother, don't take it hard
If I spend my youth a-roaming,
Rallialei ja raailei,
If I spend my youth a-roaming.

Back I will come for my only love,
She's so sweet, I can't betray her,
Rallialei ja raailei,
She's so sweet, I can't betray her.

What light is that, shining far at sea?
It's a fisher's lantern shining,
Rallialei ja raailei,
It's a fisher's lantern shining.

Mikä tuolla merellä pilkottaa?
Se on kalastajan tuli
Rallialei ja raailei,
Se on kalstajan tuli.

Älä sure pappa ja älä sure mamma,
Jos nuorena maita kuljen,
Rallialei ja raailei,
Jos nuorena maita kuljen.

Meinasin tyttöjä narrata
vaan minut petti uni,
Rallialei ja raailei,
Vaan minut petti uni.

Mikä tuolla merellä pilkottaa?
Se taitaapi olla saari,
Rallialei ja raailei,
Se taitaapi olla saari.

All Alone

In a boat rigged with sails of scarlet
I could travel across the sea.
What a mountain of gold and silver
I would bring him who waits for me!
What a mountain of gold and silver
I would bring him who waits for me!

Then how gladly I'd throw the shuttle
Weaving cloth for the pastor's shirt.
On my finger the ring would sparkle—
Oh, I am such a silly girl!
On my finger the ring would sparkle—
Oh, I am such a silly girl!

Yksin istun ja lauleskelen
Aikan' on niin ikävä;
Vesi seisoo ja linnut laulaa,
Eikä tuulikaan vedätä.
Vesi seisoo ja linnut laulaa,
Eikä tuulikaan vedätä.

Oisko pursi ja punapurjeet,
Millä mennä merten taa,
Tuolta touttaisin sulholleni
Ko'on kultaa ja hopiaa.
Tuolta tuottaisin sulholleni
Ko'on kultaa ja hopiaa.

Sitten kutoa helskyttäisin
Papinpaitakangasta,
Kihlasormus se kiilteleisi,
Voi mua hullua neitoa!
Kihlasormus se kiilteleisi,
Voi mua hullua neitoa!

Come Back to Me

There in the king's gold-en pal-ace they keep him.

There in the pal-ace I dare not go seek him.

O my be-lov-ed, my bird ev-er sing-ing, Come

back to me a-gain, back to me a-gain!

Many fair maids there—he need not be lonely.
But my beloved has eyes for me only.
O my beloved, my bird ever singing,
Come back to me again, back to me again!

Birds sing their joy in the woods where I hide me.
No joy for me but to have him beside me!
O my beloved, my bird ever singing,
Come back to me again, back to me again!

When will these long days of waiting be over?
When shall I walk once again with my lover?
O my beloved, my bird ever singing,
Come back to me again, back to me again!

Tuoll' on mun kultani ain' yhä tuolla
Kuninkaan kultaisen kartanon puolla.
Voi minun kultani, voi minun lintuni,
Kun et tule jo, kun et tule jo!

On siellä tyttöjä, on komioita,
Kultani silmät ei katsele noita.
Voi minun kultani, voi minun lintuni,
Kun et tule jo, kun et tule jo!

Linnut ne laulavat sorialla suulla,
Soriampi sivullani ääni on kuulla.
Voi minun kultani, voi minun lintuni,
Kun et tule jo, kun et tule jo!

Oi, koska näen minä sen ilopäivän,
Kultani sivullani astuvan ja käyvän?
Voi minun kultani, voi minun lintuni,
Kun et tule jo, kun et tule jo!

Tule, tule kultani, tule kotipuoleen,
Taikka jo menehynkin ikävään ja huoleen.
Voi minun kultani, voi minun lintuni,
Kun et tule jo, kun et tule jo!

The Rosebush

Oh, how gladly he'd pick it, that blooming rose,
Take it with him to cheer the way.
Oh, how gladly he'd pick it, that blooming rose,
Take it with him to cheer the way.
He was just a poor farmhand, he did not dare,
So he left it upon the spray.
He was just a poor farmhand, he did not dare,
So he left it upon the spray.

Yksi ruusu on kasvanut laaksossa
Ja se kauniisti kukoistaa.
Yksi ruusu on kasvanut laaksossa
Ja se kauniisti kukoistaa.
Yksi kulkijapoika on nähnyt sen,
Eikä voi sitä unhoittaa.
Yksi kulkijapoika on nähnyt sen,
Eikä voi sitä unhoittaa.

Ja sen olisi kyllä hän poiminut
Ja sen painanut povelleen,
Ja sen olisi kyllä hän poiminut
Ja sen painanut povelleen,
Mutta köyhänä ei ole tohtinut,
Vaan on jättänyt paikoilleen.
Mutta köyhänä ei ole tohtinut,
Vaan on jättänyt paikoilleen.

We've Had a Dance

But, of all the girls, the best one was Mi - na.

Wille—he looks like a silly,
He's a sly fox, though, our Wille—
Took Mina out in the unlighted hallway to smack her.
And the noise when they kissed was appalling,
Ev'ryone thought rain was falling!
Black as any spade my heart turned, or blacker.

Ulla, the leech, like a mourner,
Chewing dry bread in the corner,
Beckoned me over beside her and said, "You're too slow, you!"
Very soon I was feeling much better.
Tickling's her game, and I let her.
"Come outside," she said, "I've something to show you."

I waste no tears over Mina.
Let her get fatter or thinner—
Let her go die, of my tears I will still be as thrifty.
As a sweetheart my Ulla's a wonder,
Happy am I that I found her,
Though her age is far the wrong side of fifty.

Kirkonkyläss' oli tanssit
Siell' oli Jussit ja Ranssit,
Siell' oli pappilan paksu Anna Stina
Oli pieniä pojan pätkii,
Paljon tyttöjä nättii,
Mutta niistä mukavin oli Miina.

Kaikki ne kävi käsityksin
Minä vain nurkassa yksin
Kukaan ei mun kanssani tahtonut tulla.
Menin minä Miinan luokse;
Miina sanoi: nyt sinä juokse;
Sulle kelpa kyllä se kuppari-Ulla.

Ville se viekas kettu,
Joll' oli naama kuin lettu
Pussasi Miinaa porstuan pimeässä.
Muiske se kuului, että
Luulin satavan vettä;
Mieleni musta oli kuin pata-ässä.

Uunilla kuppari-Ulla
Pureskeli ranskanpullaa;
Sinne se viittasi minuakin vierahaksi.
Alkoipa toinen, peli;
Ulla mua kutkutteli;
Tuumi, että: meitähän ois' vain kaksi.

A Ring Around Her Finger

Lately I walked in the blooming fields
Where spring her sweets discloses.
Lately I walked in the blooming fields
Where spring her sweets discloses.
There was a girl, one lovely girl!
And I watched her picking the roses.
There was a girl, one lovely girl!
And I watched her picking the roses.

Watching her hands, I saw something shine,
A ring around her finger.
Watching her hands, I saw something shine,
A ring around her finger.
Sharp as a knife, it pierced my heart.
Ah, the pains I felt, still they linger.
Sharp as a knife, it pierced my heart.
Ah, the pains I felt, still they linger.

Deep are my pains, but to no one else
On earth will I reveal them.
Deep are my pains, but to no one else
On earth will I reveal them.
Only dark woods and shining sky,
Only they shall know that I feel them.
Only dark woods and shining sky,
Only they shall know that I feel them.

Taivas on sininen ja valkoinen
Ja tähtösiä täynnä.
Taivas on sininen ja valkoinen
Ja tähtösiä täynnä.
Niin on nuori sydämeni
Ajatuksia täynnä.
Niin on nuori sydämeni
Ajatuksia täynnä.

Kulkeissani vainiolla
Kukkaiskedon poikki
Kulkeissani vainiolla
Kukkaiskedon poikki
Näin minä tytön ihanan joka
Ruususia noukki.
Näin minä tytön ihanan joka
Ruususia noukki.

Näin minä hänen sormessansa
Sormuksen, joka kiilsi
Näin minä hänen sormessansa
Sormuksen, joka kiilsi
Niinkuin veitsi sydäntäni
Se kipeästi viilsi.
Niinkuin veitsi sydäntäni
Se kipeästi viilsi.

Enkä mä muille ilmoita
Mun sydänsurujani,
Enkä mä muille ilmoita
Mun sydänsurujani,
Synkkä metsä, kirkas taivas
Ne tuntevat huoliani.
Synkkä metsä, kirkas taivas
Ne tuntevat huoliani.

At the Cherry Tree

Death, come and hide my falling tears,
Close my eyes, I would never waken.
Death, come and hide my falling tears,
Close my eyes, I would never waken.
Death, I will have no friend but you,
Only friend of a heart forsaken.
Death, I will have no friend but you,
Only friend of a heart forsaken.

Tuomi onvirran reunalla,
Jonka juurella minä itkin
Tuomi onvirran reunalla,
Jonka juurella minä itkin
Vieraille maille kultani läksi
Ja jätti mun tänne yksin.
Vieraille maille kultani läksi
Ja jätti mun tänne yksin.

Kätke tuoni kyyneleen'
Sulje kuolo silmäseni,
Kätke tuoni kyyneleen'
Sulje kuolo silmäseni,
Ole sitten ystävän'
Koska jäin minä yksinäni.
Ole sitten ystävän'
Koska jäin minä yksinäni.

The Birch Tree

Lone - ly in the for - est stands a birch tree,
Stands as though for - got - ten whol - ly.
So the man who's al - ways go - ing spree - ing
Finds his home life far from jol - ly!

Stars and crescent moon appear and vanish,
In among them clouds are fleeting.
Stars and crescent moon appear and vanish,
In among them clouds are fleeting.
Other girls I greet with just a hand-shake,
Kisses are my true-love's greeting.
Other girls I greet with just a hand-shake,
Kisses are my true-love's greeting.

Ah, what grief I feel, what heavy sorrow!
Can I make you understand, dear?
Ah, what grief I feel, what heavy sorrow!
Can I make you understand, dear?
Nothing you can do will end my sorrow
Till the day I win your hand, dear.
Nothing you can do will end my sorrow
Till the day I win your hand, dear.

166

Ah, what grief I feel, what heavy sorrow!
Can I make you understand, dear?
Ah, what grief I feel, what heavy sorrow!
Can I make you understand, dear?
Nothing you can do will end my sorrow
Till the day I win your hand, dear.
Nothing you can do will end my sorrow
Till the day I win your hand, dear.

Koivu on metsässä yksinänsä,
Niinkuin unhoitettu,
Koivu on metsässä yksinänsä,
Niinkuin unhoitettu,
Niin on myös se hulivilipoika
Kodista vieroitettu.
Niin on myös se hulivilipoika
Kodista vieroitettu.

Kaksi oli tähteä taivahalla
Ja toinen puoli kuuta;
Kaksi oli tähteä taivahalla
Ja toinen puoli kutta;
Muille tytöille kättä annan
Mut omalle kullalle suuta.
Muille tytöille kättä annan
Mut omalle kullalle suuta.

Suuri ou suru ja raskas on murhe,
Huojenna kultaiseni!
Suuri ou suru ja raskas on murhe,
Huojenna kultaiseni!
Ei se ennen huojene
Kun saan sinut omakeseni.
Ei se ennen huojene
Kun saan sinut omakeseni.

Lettish and Lithuanian

LATVIA AND LITHUANIA ARE — or rather, have been — two small independent states in the marshy woodland country bordering the Baltic Sea. Their kindred languages have been local dialects since the sixteenth century, when Luther's catechism was the first printed book in each tongue. After the First World War these peoples had their first real chance at self-government, but they were so depleted by the ravages of hostilities that autonomy was difficult, if not impossible. Inevitably the larger European powers controlled the foreign policies, and so also the trade and the material prosperity of the tiny nations. They are largely agricultural states, and could never hope to be self-supporting. This fact has made it difficult for all the lesser nations of Europe, even with regional *ententes,* to develop the independent spirit and ambition which began to grow amid the adversities of alien rule. As long as power politics prevail, such states seem doomed to be pawns of their larger brothers.

Unlike the Bohemians and Poles, who once enjoyed sovereignty and lost it, the Letts were serfs whose only sense of identity lay in the hardship of their common lot. They were controlled by the Teutonic Knights until 1562, then by Poland and Sweden during the next two centuries, and by Russia from the third partition of Poland in 1795 until the Latvian state was created in 1918. Since 1939 all the Baltic states have been occupied successively by Russia and Germany and then, again, Russia.

The history of Lithuania to the south is not unlike that of her sister nation. The Grand Duchy of Lithuania was for several centuries a large and almost autonomous state stretching from the Baltic nearly to the Black Sea. It was allied with Poland until the eighteenth-century partitions erased both countries as political entities. Most of the Lithuanian population fell to Russia, and the Pan-Slavic ideas of culture and history were applied to them even more severely than to the Poles. The old Polish legal code was replaced by Russian laws; in 1849 the name Lithuania was officially replaced by "Northwestern Territory"; and after an uprising in 1863 no books were allowed to be printed in Lithuanian for forty years.

Yet it was largely amidst Russian opposition that the educational awakening begun in the eighteenth century assumed important proportions among both peoples. Folklore was a particular inheritance which was valued as something no government edict or foreign *kultur* could take away. The nineteenth century saw important collections of Latvian and Lithuanian songs, proverbs and folk tales, at a time when these Baltic states seemed fated to lose their very identity.

There is an old saying that the Lithuanian

serf, like the eel, can draw his skin over his ears. And during the years when the language could be printed only in Russian characters, there was a steady traffic in illegal volumes which were imported into the country from Tilsit, all dated "Vilna, 1863" as a token of the days before censorship. The schoolmasters lived with one family after another, teaching the children their own language and customs, singing the native songs with the whole family, then moving on before the Russian authorities interfered.

Nowhere is the character of a whole people more accurately and completely mirrored than in the *daina* (plural: Lithuanian *dainos*, Latvian *dainas*), or secular song of the two nations. They are beautifully lyrical, with only the slightest suggestion of specific narrative. Rather, they contain reflections on almost every sort of human activity of the race, and so without describing a particular set of actions they imply an almost universal knowledge of the peasant mind and heart. Through these lyrics we see peoples still clinging to pagan superstitions, relatively unimpressed by the late arrival of Christianity. We see the life of the poor farmer rooted to the soil, keenly conscious of the simple outdoors. Water and forests, livestock and harvest, industrious or lazy family, and the unending round of birth, marriage and death are the commonplaces of the poor. They constitute the subject-matter of almost all domestic folksong, but in few parts of the world are simplicity and intensity of feeling so well blended.

The very delicate poetic effects produced in the *daina* of both nations are not wholly a conscious creation. They are almost inescapable by the very nature of the language, with its light vowels, its numerous case endings and diminutives which make assonance, rhyme and alliteration almost impossible to avoid. The haunting echoic effect can scarcely be dupli-

cated in translation to any other language. Diminutives if multiplied soon become vulgar, and yet where the echo is not present, much of the gossamer overtone of the original is lost.

The themes of the Latvian and Lithuanian *daina* are similar, though the accent of the two languages differs slightly, the melodies are not quite alike, and the poems assume individual forms. Chiefly notable is the epigrammatic quality of the Latvian *dainas*. Most of them are of two long lines (usually printed as quatrains). Yet in such a small compass there is frequently all the overtone of implication that one finds in an elaborate poem. Here are two examples which show a distillation of thought and emotion:

> *Little dove, fly over the estate,*
> *Confuse the speech of squires*
> *When they sit in judgment*
> *On my youngest brother.*

And

> *If you want pure water,*
> *Draw it from the bottom of the well.*
> *If you want a young bride*
> *From the cradle take the child.*[1]

The second of these *dainas* is interesting for an additional reason, for it shows one typical device of composition. The parallelism between external nature and human life is exploited here, so that each is a commentary on the other.

In the longer Lithuanian *dainos*, more narrative traces are likely to remain, though the feeling is usually more important than the action. Symbolism abounds in both nations. The floral wreath (of "I Will Tell You," "Sister, the Sun Is Rising," "Oh How He Scolded"), usually of roses in Latvia, always of rue in Lithuania, symbolizes the innocence of the unmarried maiden. She is careful not to lose it, not to

---

[1] U. Katzenelenbogen, *The Daina* (Chicago, 1935), pp. 144, 150; translated from the monumental collection of 218,000 Latvian *dainas* edited by Kr. Barons and H. Wissendorff.

allow it to become wet with dew (a sign that she had been out all night), and not to allow it to be trampled on. When she marries, her flowing hair is bound by a matron's hood, and she gives her wreath to a younger sister or a bridesmaid. The young man's horse is a symbol of his virility and boldness; if it is treated kindly by the parents of his beloved, he knows he is approved. In our "The Pledged Horse," the lover, who is obviously being encouraged, has sealed a bargain with his future mother-in-law by letting her have his horse. If the horse in the stable refuses to eat, trouble may be brewing between the young man and his beloved ("Little Horse of Mine").

Most of the *dainas* and *dainos* have been created by women, though they are sung by everyone. The men compose folk-tales and in alehouses sing burlesquing and obscene songs which most collectors consider street music and not genuine folk song. There are, to be sure, some satiric and mildly ribald examples of genuine *daina;* but the dominant tone is one of delicacy and innocence. The song-contest is common in Latvia, where the lyrics are so short. When a subject is proposed, the singer who takes it up attempts to recall a dozen songs on that subject, and if he fails, another will try to sing a dozen fresh *dainas*. The old saying, "Before we finish singing one, we have nine more in our heads," must have had ample justification in fact.

Musically the songs of both countries are elegiac in character, as Katzenelenbogen has pointed out.[1] Many of them are based on minor or modal scales. The Latvian melodies are short, usually eight measures. The Lithuanian, presenting more signs of musical antiquity, are the more frequently modal ("Little Horse of Mine," "Husband and Wife," "Long I Have Woven," all in the Aeolian mode). Many

[1] *Op. cit.,* p. 30.

of the tunes are made up of compressed phrases (cf. "Oh How He Scolded," fifteen measures, and "Long I Have Woven," ten measures). In contour and in general feeling the Baltic melodies have almost nothing in common with the more southerly nations of the continent.

"The Bee Tree" is a love song, but not merely that. Katzenelenbogen says that many of the peasants kept bees, the hives usually being in tree-trunks or rotten stumps. The third stanza implies not only an ill-omen for romantic love, but also a bad year for the bee-keeper. The motif of the girl in love with the bee-keeper's son is common in the Latvian *daina.*

"I Will Tell You" is elusive, but we seem to have here a kind of female Hiawatha, completely attuned to nature, able to understand flowers and streams. The theme is not unlike that of some of the mythological songs to be found in any Latvian collection.

"Who Is Crying?" is to be classed as an orphan-song. This subject is frequently developed in connection with war, which leaves the peasant children fatherless. The hostilities are always far away in the old songs, and there is no evidence that father and son realize why or whom they are fighting. Fatalistically the people accept war as an inevitable part of life. It is never portrayed glamorously; always it is equated with death. Here the poverty of the orphans occupies the singer, and the song introduces the familiar motif of the sun and the other elements as the orphans' only kin.

"Sister, the Sun Is Rising" is a Lithuanian *daina* with as much narrative content as one usually finds. In folksong the family of the groom are usually spoken of as strangers, and ordinarily we are to expect the bride to be unhappy among them. Here the bride's brothers escort her faithfully, but after the wedding they cannot rescue her from her suffering. "Oh How He Scolded" is another *daina* of an unhappy bride. "Husband and Wife" shows us a vignette of married life from the husband's point of view. With his horsewhip he is able to teach his bride so much about spinning and weaving that the relatives will no more say that he has married a lazy wife.

The parallelism between nature and human feelings is illustrated by the weaver and the broken shuttle in "Long I Have Woven." The weaving symbolizes longing for another, and the breaking of the shuttle signifies that the girl's hopes are thus far in vain. The ideal of a good wife, as seen in the last stanza, makes us realize how rude was the life of the peasant, and how pathetic the contrast between reality and dreams.

I Will Tell You

Where a flowing brooklet whispers,
Pretty flowers show their faces.
So, wherever someone listens,
Someone else his secret tells.

As a bee goes gath'ring honey,
So I gather what is spoken.
Then I fasten words together,
Like a wreath made all of bloom.

When I've made my flower-garland,
Open one by one the flowers.
When I fasten words together,
People like my words to hear.

Teizi, teizi, walodiņa,
Ko upite burbuleja,
Ko upite burbuleja,
Ko pogaja lakstigal'!

Kur upite burbuleja,
Tur usplauka pumpuriņi;
Kur ļautiņi klausijasi,
Tur walodas daudsinaj'!

Kà bitite medu suhza,
Tà es ļauschu walodiņu.
Es saliku wahrdu seedus
Kà puķites wainagà.

Seedi paschi usseedeja,
Es nopinu wainadsiņu.
Wisi ļaudis klausijasi,
Kad es teizu walodiņ'.

The Bee Tree

Tender are her cheeks as flowers,
Soft her hands as wax new-moulded.
Now the tree is disappearing,
Now you'll hear her cry and scold:

"Bees, without you, we are helpless,
Summer's joys will go to ruin.
We need you as you need flowers.
Flowers gone, what could you do?"

Upe nesa osoliņu ar wisami bititemi,
Upe nesa osoliņu ar wisami bititem.

Drawineeka lihgawiņa tek gar malu raudadama,
Drawineeka lihgawiņa tek gar malu raudadam'.

Seedu swahrki mugurâi, wasku zimdi rozinâi
Seedu swahrki mugurâi, wasku zimdi rozinâ.

Truhka, truhka tew, bitite, ja tew truhka, truhks man ari,
Truhka, truhka tew, bitite, ja tew truhka, truhks man ar.

Kad tew truhka silâ seedu, truhks man wasku rituliņa,
Kad tew truhka silâ seedu, truhks man wasku rituliņ'.

The Pledged Horse

Other men are busy sowing.
Not a furrow in my field yet!
How without my horse to help me
Can I ever plow my field?

As a pledge I gave my sorrel.
Since my sweetheart's mother took him,
None can ask for her, no matter
How well filled his money-bag.

Tumschâ naktî, saļâ sahlê laukâ laischu kumeliņa,
Tumschâ naktî, saļâ sahlê laukâ laischu kumeliņ'.

Nu, Deewiņi, tawâ siņâ, nu tawâsi roziņâsi,
Nu, Deewiņi, tawâ siņâ, nu tawâsi roziņâs.

Ziti wihri rudsus sehja, man ziliņas neezetas,
Ziti wihri rudsus sehja, man ziliņas neezet's.

Ko ezeschu es ziliņas, naw man behra kumeliņa,
Ko ezeschu es ziliņas, naw man behra kumeliņ'.

Kihlam dewu meitu mahtei sawu behro kumeliņu,
Kihlam dewu meitu mahtei sawu behro kumeliņ'.

Lai zitami neapsola patihkamo lihgawiņu,
Lai zitami neapsola patihkamo lihgawiņ'.

Who Is Crying?

Who is cry-ing? What lam-ent-ing sounds so sad-ly through the night?

They are or-phan child-ren cry-ing, bowed be-neath their mas-ter's might.

Crying sadly, see them making little fires against the cold.
By the river, see them bending, dipping bread-crusts hard and old.

Sun, this evening when you leave us, all of gold your boat will be.
But tomorrow, at your rising, sails of crimson I shall see.

Sun so golden, will you tell me where you wandered yesterday?
"I was warming shiv'ring orphans in the mountains far away."

Kas tee tahdi, kas dseedaja bes saulites wakarâ?
Tee ir wisi bahra behrni, bahrgu kungu klausitaj'!

Kurin' ugun', silda gaisu, slauka gauschas asaras,
Krimta zeetu pelaw'maisi, awotiņâ mehrzedam'.

Saulit' wehlu wakarâi sehschas selta laiwiņâ;
Rihtâ agri uslehkdama, atstahj laiwu lihgojot.

Kam, saulite, wehlu lehzi, kur tik ilgi kawejees?
Ais wiņeemi kalniņeemi, bahra behrnus sildidam'.

Little Horse of Mine

"Is it for your oat-bin you are longing?
Do you long to nibble clover white?
Is it to the brookside you would go,
Where the water runs clear and bright?"

"Not for oats or stable am I longing,
Neither would I nibble clover white.
Only to the brookside would I go,
Where the water runs clear and bright."

Oi ko žvengi, žirgeli,
Oi ko žvengi, bėrasai?
Oi ko žvengi žirgužėli,
Iš stoineles vedamas?

Ar tau gailu avižų?
Ar baltųjų dobilų?
Ar tau gailu srovės upių
Ir tyro vandenėlio?

Nei man gailu avižų,
Nei baltųjų dobilų,
Tik man gailu srovės upių
Ir tyrų vandenėlių.

Sister, the Sun Is Rising

"Sis — ter, the sun is ris — ing, Sis — ter, the dawn is break — ing! Rise, rise, my sis — ter, guest ev — er cher — ished, Is it not time for wak — ing?

wak ing?" griev ing

178

"Weave now a wreath of flowers,
Fit your smooth forehead to crown, dear.
See your white brothers, guests ever cherished,
Saddling their horses brown, dear.
See your white brothers, guests ever cherished,
Saddling their horses brown, dear."

As I through fields went riding,
Fields that were all my mother's,
Guiding me onward, giving me comfort,
Rode at my side my brothers.
Guiding me onward, giving me comfort,
Rode at my side my brothers.

As I through fields went riding,
Fields that were all his mother's,
Guiding me onward, giving me insults,
Rode at my side his brothers.
Guiding me onward, giving me insults,
Rode at my side his brothers.

Then to the house they brought me—
House of my bridegroom's mother.
There at her gateway, waiting, I felt it—
All that I here would suffer.
There at her gateway, waiting, I felt it—
All that I here would suffer.

Would that my brothers knew it—
Even my youngest brother.
Quick he'd come riding, quick to defend me,
End all that here I suffer.
Quick he'd come riding, quick to defend me,
End all that here I suffer.

Came then my youngest brother—
Came, and his sword unsheathing,
Struck at the gateway, shattered his sword-blade.
No one can end my grieving.
Struck at the gateway, shattered his sword-blade.
No one can end my grieving.

Beauštanti aušrele
Betekanti saulelė,
Kelk, seserele, mano viešnele,
Ar tu dar neišmiegojai?
Kelk, seserele, mano viešnele,
Ar tu dar neišmiegojai?

Pinkis vainikėlį
Dėkis ant galvelės,
Tavo sveteliai, balti broleliai,
Balnoj bėrus žirgelius.
Tavo sveteliai, balti broleliai,
Balnoj bėrus žirgelius.

Kad vaziavau per lauką
Motinėlės laukelį,
Šalimis jojo balti broleliai
Seselę ramindami.
Šalimis jojo balti broleliai
Seselę ramindami.

Privažiavau dvarelį
Anytėlės vartelius,
Aš ir pamačiau savo vargelį
Anytėlės varteliuos.
Aš ir pamačiau savo vargelį
Anytėlės varteliuos.

Oh, How He Scolded

Came my old father, walking so steady,
Holding a horsewhip, holding it ready.
"Don't you dare scold her, don't you dare hit her!
Not yet she's yours, young fellow!

Came then my mother, walking so steady,
Holding a horsewhip, holding it ready.
"Scold her and beat her, early and often!
Now she is yours, and welcome!"

Came then my sister, walking so lightly,
Holding a rue-branch, holding it tightly.
"Scold her and beat her, early and often!
Now she is yours, dear brother!"

Tai mane mušė, tai nemylėjo,
Tai mane barė, tai negailėjo:
Oi, eisiu, eisiu aš pasiskūsiu
Savam senam tėveliui

Mano tėvelis tai ateidamas,
Rankoj rykštelę atsinešdamas:
Oi, nemušk, nebark, žente, dukrelės
Dar ne tavo valelė.

Mano motulė tai ateidama,
Rankoj rykštelę atnešdama:
Oi, muški, barki, žente, dukrelę
Dabar tavo valelė.

Mano sesulė tai ateidama,
Rankoj rūtelę atsinešdama:
Tai muški, barki, švogeriau, sesulę,
Tai dabar tavo valelė.

By My Window

In the boat a sailor,
Only one young sailor,
He his face was washing—
White sea-foam it was he washed in.
He his face was washing
In the salt white sea-foam.

Next he fell to combing,
Hair with fish-combs combing,
Then from off his finger
Took a ring and threw it over,
Watched the ocean take it,
Watched it sinking, sinking.

"Float, my little ring, now,
Go, my little ring, now,
Seek a foreign country.
Go until you find the country
Where my bride awaits me—
Go and find that country."

Sėdžiu už stalelio,
Žiūriu pro langeli,
Čiūčiuoja liūliuoja
Ant mariu laivelis.
Čiūčiuoja liūliuoja
Ant mariu laivelis.

O tame laively
Bernelis sėdėjo,
Mareliu putelėms
Sau burnele prausė.
Mareliu putelėms
Sau burnele prausė.

Mareliu putelėms
Sau burnele prausė,
Žuveliu šukelėms
Galvele šukavo.
Žuveliu šukelėms
Galvele šukavo.

Žuveliu šukelėms
Galvele šukavo,
Skandino žiedeli
I mariu dugneli.
Skandino žiedeli
I mariu dugneli.

Plauki sau, žiedeli
Svetimon šalelėn,
Svetimon šalelėn,
Kur mano mergelė.
Svetimon šalelėn,
Kur mano mergelė.

Husband and Wife

"Wife," I said, "you'll nev-er find me In-to tem-pers fly-ing."

Late-ly, though, I had to scold her. She spent three days cry-ing.

Late-ly, though, I had to scold her. She spent three days cry-ing.

"Hush, don't cry, my little darling—
Really I regret it.
I have such a nice new horsewhip!
Let me go and get it.
I have such a nice new horsewhip!
Let me go and get it.

"Now I'll teach you, little darling—
By this whip I swear it—
How to spin and weave fine linen,
Also how to wear it.
How to spin and weave fine linen,
Also how to wear it.

"Now, for lack of shirts and aprons,
We'll no more bemoan us.
Now our uncles, aunts and cousins
Will be glad to own us!
Now our uncles, aunts and cousins
Will be glad to own us!"

Aš paėmiau mergužėlę,
Ketinau nebarti,
Tik pabariau vieną kartą
Tris dieneles verkė.
Tik pabariau vieną kartą
Tris dieneles verkė.

Cit, neverki, mergužėle,
Jau daugiau nebarsiu:
Karo svirne kančiukėlis,
Aš jį nusikarsiu.
Karo svirne kančiukėlis,
Aš jį nusikarsiu.

Išmokinsiu, mergužėle,
Spartų darbą dirbti,
Plonai verpti, tankiai austi
Ir gražiai nešioti.
Plonai verpti, tankiai austi
Ir gražiai nešioti.

Kad man būtų marškinėliai,
O tau prijuostėlė,
Kad nebūtų sarmatėlės
Tarpe giminėlių.
Kad nebūtų sarmatėlės
Tarpe giminėlių.

Long I Have Woven

Sostenuto e espressivo

Long I have wov – en, Wov – en and wov – en, Mak – ing fine lin – en, Ply – ing my thread and my map – le shut – tle.

Thread I have broken,
Broken my shuttle,
Here they lie broken.
Not for a rich boy my heart is broken.

Broken my heart is,
Not for a rich boy.
I love a poor boy.
Poor from the cradle, his life's a hard one.

Trouble and hardship,
Trouble and hardship,
Well has he known them,
Left a poor orphan, brought up by strangers.

Plowing is hard, but
Well I can do it,
Well guide the oxen.
That and much more I will do to help him.

Vai, audžiau, audžiau
Plonas drobeles
Žalios nendrės skietely,
Klevine šaudyklėle.

Sulaužiau skietą
Ir šaudyklėlę,
Nepalaužiau širdelės
Ant bagoto bernelio.

Vai, tik palaužiau
Savo širdelę
Ant vargo bernelio
Ant jos vargo dienelių.

Kuris papratęs
Vargelį vargti
Iš maženų dienelių,
Ant svetimų rankelių.

Oi, arsiu, arsiu
Ir pakartosiu
Ant pūdymo laukelio
Su palšais jauteliais.

Sulaužiau žagrę
Ir pažagrėlę,
Nepalauziau sirdelės
Ant bagotos mergelės.

Vai, tik palaužiau
Savo širdelę
Ant vargo mergelės,
Ant jos vargo dienelių.

Katra papratus
Vargelį vargti
Iš maženų dienelių,
Ant svetimų rankelių.

Russian and Ukrainian

IF WE THINK of Russia in its most inclusive sense, we have to do with the largest continuous political entity in the world, occupying alone one-seventh of the earth's land mass. So extensive and varied is the Soviet Union that no modest-sized volume could hope to illustrate its wealth of folksong; and no brief essay can do more than sketch in outline what is to be found within its borders. Even limiting our attention to the European districts formerly known as Great Russia and Little Russia (the Ukraine), we are faced with all the heterogeneity of a sub-continent, as large as all the rest of Europe.

According to almost all Western standards, Russia (which for convenience we shall use to mean Russia-in-Europe) has been very backward. Serfdom was not abolished until 1861 (it is perhaps unfair to recall that in America the Emancipation Proclamation was issued in 1863). In 1926 more than half the Russian inhabitants were yet illiterate. Death rates have been criminally high, standards of sanitation and domestic economy shocking. The reason lies partly in the fact that Russia is predominantly an agricultural nation. More than four-fifths of her population live on farms, and the highly developed civilization of some of the Western countries (with the attendant evils) has been duplicated in only a few cities.

Soviet Russia has, then, remained a land of peasants to this day.

Russian folksong is plentiful and, in the main, unwesternized. Since the days of Peter the Great (1672-1725) the upper classes have been conscious of Berlin and Paris; most of the musicians affected an international style which was largely the product of Italy and Germany. The peasants, so far removed socially from their superiors, were not affected by these eighteenth century efforts to cosmopolitanize Russia. Indeed, education and enlightenment were carefully and systematically denied the lower classes, lest knowledge breed discontent. When the collectors began early in the nineteenth century to assemble the national folksong, they found a dynamic and vigorous tradition of heroic as well as lyric song. Later, when the great musical rebirth began, musicians such as Balakirev, Rimsky-Korsakov, Tchaikovsky and others transcribed and edited collections.

Most important for Russia's musical renaissance, Glinka early in the nineteenth century showed how folk tunes, freed from inappropriate Italianate harmonies, could be used as serious thematic material. He was enthusiastic over the wealth of melody embodying the racial spirit, saying, "The people invent, composers only arrange." He held that his colleagues should be proud of their racial heritage and should write like Russians, not as if they were composers of Vienna or Leipzig or Berlin. The unreceptive upper-class greeted his popular first opera, *A Life for the Czar* (1836), coldly; "Coachmen's music," they called it. But Glinka paved the way for the extensive, if frequently self-conscious, use of folk idiom in later orchestral and operatic compositions. Moussorgsky and Tchaikovsky, Borodin, Rimsky-Korsakov and more recently Stravinsky have drawn inspiration from simple lyric tunes. It is the fault of romantic fashion, and not of the folk melodies themselves, that they are

sometimes employed in pretentious and bombastic contexts (as is the dance tune in the final movement of the Tchaikovsky *Fourth Symphony*).

Oldest among this unsurpassed wealth of folk material are the heroic songs, called *byliny*. They are of the same general character as the Spanish *romanceros*, the Yugoslavian "Heroic songs" (*junačke pesme*), the Finnish *runos*, and they are paralleled in the south by the Ukrainian *dumy*. The *byliny*, which recount epic adventures of old kings and legendary heroes, seem to have been once the fashionable entertainment of the gentry, if one may judge by occasional details in the songs themselves; but they are now sung only by peasants. The best *byliny* singers are old men, often blind, who delight in their prowess and their memory. Most of them know only two or three recitative-tunes to which they chant all their *byliny*. The repertoire of the ablest singers seems endless.[1]

Apart from these narrative songs in epic style, there are many kinds of lyrics which the present collection can illustrate only in part. Rimsky-Korsakov published a hundred representative songs which show the range of the Russian folk muse. Beside the *byliny* he included three large classes of lyrical pieces: festival songs, dancing songs, and general lyrics. The festival group is by far the largest and is in some respects the most interesting. Like almost all the other Eastern European peoples, the Russians make every holiday and special festival a sort of *Singspiel*. For Christmastide there are special songs (*koliada*) that young people sing as they march from house to house in the villages on Christmas eve, and there are other conventional pieces for the remainder of the twelve-day celebration. Carnival time (be-

---

[1] For an interesting account of a recent (1928-29) contest between two superb *byliny* singers, see H. M. and N. K. Chadwick, *The Growth of Literature*, II (Cambridge, 1936), 241-243.

fore Lent), Easter, the beginning of Spring, and church holidays such as Pentecost, Trinity Sunday and Ascension Day all have their appropriate verses. And so elaborate is the musical background of weddings that Rimsky-Korsakov devoted thirty of his hundred songs to this occasion alone. Beginning with the evening before the wedding, when songs of courtship, love at first sight (cf. "Novgorod's Bells"), and prophecies of life's vicissitudes are sung, these songs run the gamut of the ceremony until the newlyweds are established at the home of the husband's parents. After the serious part of the ceremony is concluded, a kind of jester can come out and sing verses of satire (or dramatic irony) concerning the pleasures of the single life or the cruelties of the mother-in-law. The Russian peasant wedding is on the whole a solemn and tearful occasion, representing important economic as well as sentimental alterations in the lives of both families.

Of the general lyrics it may be said that Russian songs treat the universal variety of subject-matter—songs of soldiers, boatmen, peddlers, farmers and other occupational groups; cradle songs and funeral dirges; songs of domestic joy or sorrow; and above all, songs of love. Like the lyrical expressions of most other Slavic peoples, they stem from a homogeneous society in which relative poverty is the norm, and in which the folkways imply a distant pagan era. The realistic pieces are songs of the outdoors, strong in energy and rooted to a code of hard work and fatalistic acceptance of appointed destiny. The romantic songs, which probably are in the majority, contain all these qualities aforementioned, plus a very noticeable penchant for escape and wish-fulfillment.

In the performance of peasant folksongs, Russia exhibits one quality which marks her off from most of Western Europe. The folk-song, we commonly say, is sung either by a single singer or in unison by a chorus. Russian song, however, seems to be polyphonic; for once the song has begun, the rest of the singers usually come in for a few measures at a time, extemporizing three or four additional melodic lines, after the manner of the Negro spiritual in its natural habitat. The national instruments of Russia include the *gusli,* a kind of zither (not to be confused with the Balkan *gusla*), and the *balalaika,* a three-stringed guitar with a long neck and a triangular body. According to a recent writer, the harmonica has now become common.

Folk music among the Ukrainians differs in some details from what we have just described. The inhabitants of Galicia and Ruthenia are markedly Western; in the southern districts, Ukrainia is close to the South Slavs and the gateway to Asia Minor. Equally important in the national character has been the traditional anti-Muscovite feeling of the Ukrainians, who have a genuine Southern pride in their history and folkways, and who fought bitterly against absorption in the old Russian Empire. The Ukraine is now (forgetting the war) an independent republic within the U.S.S.R., but still self-consciously guards her own integrity.

The Ukrainian equivalent of the epic *byliny* is the *duma* or *dumka,* differing from its northern counterpart in being usually rhymed, and in being chanted in recitativo-style to the accompaniment of the *cobza,* a twenty-stringed lute. The subject-matter often centers upon the Cossack expeditions against Turks or Poles. The later examples of both varieties of heroic song are sometimes elegiac, but usually tend to resemble the journalistic ballads of the West. Musically the old *dumy* employ slender resources—often only three or four notes—and show a kinship with Balkan recitative in their Oriental flavoring and constantly changing, irregular rhythm.

The lyrical songs might have originated almost anywhere, but show the particular stamp of Czechs or Poles or the Balkans wherever the circumstantial evidence is definite. But this is not to say that the Ukrainians have been merely imitative; rather, they have been able to assimilate, to retain a distinctive idiom, no matter what alien elements overlie the fundamental.

Much has been written about the "uncertain tonality" of Russian music, and of the possible modal character of the scales. The best modern opinion is disinclined to press the modal affiliation, and to hold, as we have already remarked, that Russian song is by inference polyphonic. What puzzles us at first is, of course, that this is not Western music, capable of harmonization along familiar lines. The Russian nationalist composers at the end of the nineteenth century —Borodin, for instance—made this clear as they developed harmonic patterns by instinct and "racial memory," not by academic rule.

"The Troika" and "Take Me, Earth" are examples of rather recent products—probably of the nineteenth-century. Both of them are cast in dancing rhythms, and the subject-matter, especially that of "The Troika," seems to belie peasant origin. The excellent tune of "Take Me, Earth" may owe something to the international gypsy idiom.

"Woman's Sad Lot," "Charm," and "Round-Dance" illustrate the common small stanza. The tunes are but eight measures long, and seem older than the foregoing Russian songs, particularly since they are not so conventionalized in their minor keys. Half of "Woman's Sad Lot" is in A minor, the other half in E minor; half of "Charm" is in major, the rest in minor. "Round-Dance" is based upon an old "gapped" scale with but six tones. Its subject-matter defines it as an old round-dance.

"Novgorod's Bells" is one of the thirty marriage songs in Rimsky-Korsakov's collection. It tells of love at first sight, and is to be sung on the evening before the wedding. Rimsky-Korsakov recorded it from the singing of his mother, who had learned it in the Orlov district, between Moscow and Kharkov. The melody of this old ballad has been used for a song in the inn scene of Moussorgsky's *Boris Godunov*. The heavy accents, which in the original imitate the bells of Novgorod, are used with humorous effect in the opera as the thick-lipped singer, in a drunken condition, stammers more or less in time.

The Ukrainian songs in our collection are considerably westernized. The influence of Polish dance rhythms and the Slovakian gaiety of minor keys both point to West Slavic influence. In "The Letter Writer" we are reminded that the professional scribe among illiterate peoples has by no means disappeared. In every American city with a large foreign population he can still be found. The reference to "Cossack" in "Cossack's Farewell" probably alludes to the nineteenth century use of the southern Russian soldiers for colonizing some of the habitable Siberian districts.

Woman's Sad Lot

Through the fields as I was go - ing, Shone the sun so
hot - ly glow - ing. Wear - y I felt oh, Wear - y I felt.

Still I trudged across the stubble.
Woman's life is full of trouble.
Woman's sad lot! Oh,
Woman's sad lot!

Far from where the men were reaping,
Soon my weary self was sleeping;
Slept and then waked—oh,
Slept and then waked.

Thus as I the time was whiling,
Came a fellow, started smiling,
Courting me, too—oh,
Courting me, too.

Long my mother waited, wondered,
Long my sister waited, pondered
Where I might be—oh,
Where I might be.

Night came down upon the stubble.
Women have all kinds of trouble!
Woman's sad lot! Oh,
Woman's sad lot!

Okak polosyn'ku ja žala,
Zoloty snopy vjazala,
I ustala, i ustala.

Istomilas', razomlela . . .
To-to naše bab'e delo,
Dolja zlaja, dolja zlaja!

Ot trevogi tolku malo,
Na snopakh ja zadremala
U dorogi, u dorogi!

Paren' tut, kak tut slucilsja,
Ukhmyl'nulsja, naklonilsja,
Stal laskat'sja, stal laskat'sja.

Muž s svekrov'ju dolgo ždali,
Mež soboju razsuzdali:
Vyžnet Maša, Vyžnet Maša.

A nad Mašej noč' temnela . . .
To-to naše bab'ė delo,
Dolja zlaja, dolja zlaja!

The Troika

Well they know without my telling
Where she lives, for whom I long.
Round their hoofs the snow is swirling.
Loud the coachman sings his song.
Round their flying hoofs the snow is swirling.
Loud the coachman sings his song.

Hurry, horses, faster, faster!
Quick, my flying hawks, away!
Days and hours like these are golden—
We must seize them while we may.
Golden days are these and golden minutes—
We must seize them while we may.

Till with age my hair starts graying,
Till my locks have ceased to curl,
Let me live in joy and gladness,
Let me love a pretty girl!
Let me live my life in joy and gladness,
Let me love a pretty girl!

Zaprjagu je trojku borzykh,
Tëmno-karikh lošadej
I pomčus' ja v noč' moroznu
Prjamo k ljubuške svoej.
Edu, edu, edu, edu k nej,
Prjamo k ljubuške svoej.

Po privyčke koni znajut,
Gde sudaruška živët.
Sneg kopytami vzryvajut,
Jamščik pesenki poët.
Sneg kopytami vzryvajut,
Jamščik pesenki poët.

Akh, vy, koni udalye,
Mčites' sokola bystrej!
Ne terjajte dni zlatye,
Ikh nemnogo v žizni sej.
Ne terjajte dni zlatye,
Ikh nemnogo v žizni sej.

Poka kudri kol 'com v'jutsja,
Budem veselo my žit'!
Poka Rusy ne sekutsja,
Budem devušek ljubit'!
Poka Rusy ne sekutsja,
Budem devušek ljubit'.

Take Me, Earth

Life without my love is nothing.
Can I choose another bride? Oh—
Fate has spoken, Fate has doomed me,
Death will lay me by her side. Oh—
Fate has spoken, Fate has doomed me,
Death will lay me by her side.

Open, earth, gray earth, our mother,
Take my youth, thy peace I crave. Oh—
Take me, earth, our mother, ţake me!
In thy lap I seek my grave—oh—
Take me, earth, our mother, take me!
In thy lap I seek my grave.

To ne veter vetku klonit,
Ne dubravuška šumit,
To moë serdečko stonet,
Kak osennij list drozit,
To moë serdečko stonet,
Kak osennij list drozit.

Izvela menja kručina,
Podkolodnaja zmeja.
Dogoraj, moja lučina,
Dogorju s tobaj i ja,
Dogoraj, moja lučina,
Dogorju s tobaj i ja.

Në žit'ë mne zdes' bez miloj!
S kem teper' pojdu k vencu?
Znat', sudil mne rok, s mogiloj
Obvenčat'sja molodcu,
Znat', sudil mne rok, s mogiloj
Obvenčat'sja molodcu.

Razstupis', zemlja syraja,
Daj mne molodcu pokoj,
Prijuti menja, rodnaja,
V temnoj kel'e grobovoj,
Prijuti menja, rodnaja,
V temnoj kel'e grobovoj!

Charm

For her sweetheart gone to far lands,
All for him she wove her garlands,
Walked and threw them back behind her—
Ancient charm to bring him home.

"Come back home, my hope, my darling,
Come back home, my heart, my starling,
Come back home and hear my riddle,
Find the answer, tell it to me!

"What makes curly hair stay curly?
What makes hair fall out too early?
 Happy people's hair stays curly.
Grief makes people lose their hair."

Belolica, kruglolica,
Krasnaja devica,
Pri dolinuške stojala,
Kalinu lomala.

Pri dolinuške stojala
Kalinu lomala.
Ja kalinušku lomala
V pučecki vjazala.

Ja v pučecki vjazala,
V dorožky brosala,
Ja v dorožen'ku brosala,
Druga vozvraščala:

Vorotis', moja nadezda!
Vorotisja serdce!
Ne vorotiš'sja, nadežda,
Khotja ogljanisja.

Round-Dance

In my garden, herbs are growing,
Now they flower, row on row.
He who has no herbs and needs them,
To my garden let him go.

Round my garden girls go dancing,
Sweet and high their voices sound.
Come and dance here, join our circle!
Everyone, come, dance our round!

Ja na kamuške sižu, ja topor v rukakh deržu,
Aj li, aj ljuli, ja topor v rukakh deržu.

Ja topor v rukakh deržu, vot ja koluški tešu,
Aj li, aj ljuli, vot ja koluški tešu.

Vot ja koluški tešu, izgorod gorožu,
Aj li, aj ljuli, izgorod gorožu.

Izgorod gorožu, ja kapustu sažu,
Aj li, aj ljuli, ja kapustu sažu.

Vse ja belen'kuju, ja kočannen'kuju,
Aj li, aj ljuli, ja kočannen'kuju.

U kogo netu kapusty, prošu k nam v ogorod,
Aj li, aj ljuli, prošu k nam v ogorod.

Prošu k nam v ogorod, vo devičij khorovod,
Aj li, aj ljuli, vo devičij khorovod.

Novgorod's Bells

Olympiada rang them that day.
Riding alone went Sir Luka, son of old Lvov.
Son of Lvov, riding alone.

Hearing them ringing, quick he drew rein.
Thralled by her beauty so wondrous, all his heart burned,
Thralled by her face, all his heart burned.

Home then he galloped. "Mother," he said,
"Mother, this day I have seen her—she is my fate.
Her I will wed, she is my fate.

"Mother, what beauty, slender and tall!
Lovely her face white and rosy, black are her brows.
Her I will wed, black are her brows."

Zvonili zvony v Novgorode,
Zvončej togo vo kamenoj Moskve,
vo kamenoj Moskve.

Zvonila zvony Alimpiaduška,
Zvonila zvony Gavrilovna.
zvony Gavrilovna.

Mimo ekhal tut Luka gospodin,
Mimo ekhal tut L'vovič,
ekhal tut L'vovič.

Zvona eja on zaslušalsja,
Krasoty eja zasmotrelsja,
eja zasmotrelsja.

Priekhal domoj stal raskazyvat':
Videl ja, matuška, svoju suženuju,
svoju suženuju.

Videl ja, sudarynja svoju rjaženuju;
Rostom ona i tonka vysoka,
i tonka vysoka.

Licom ona i bela i rumjana,
Brot' ju ona počernee menja,
počernee menja.

Ah, That Day

200

All the other girls and fellows
Plague me when we chance to meet.
"What's the matter, friend?" they ask me,
"Seems you're always on the street!"
Then among themselves they whisper,
Nod and smile, or wink and shove.
Next to guess will be the servants.
All the world will know I love!
Next to guess will be the servants.
All the world will know I love!

Pijšov ja raz na ulycju,
Ta tepera kajus',
Poljubyv ja djivčynon'ku,
Ta dosyža khajus'.
Serce mljije, zavmyraje,
Khoč nerad, ta plaču,
Jak svojeji mylen'koji
Khoč den' ne pobaču,
Jak svojeji mylen'koji
Khoč den' ne pobaču!

Elder Blooming

"I will tell you! Take your answer:
All the while we're walking,
Though my body walks beside you,
Though my body walks beside you,
Heart to *him* is talking."

Červonaja kalynon'ka,
Bily derevce
Čom do mene ne hovoryš,
Čom do mene ne hovoryš
Moje ljube serce?

The Letter Writer

If my moth-er had not seen me, I'd have gone,
I'm not bash-ful. She was there, though, so I did-n't.
How I wish she had-n't been!

He's a scribe, a letter-writer,
Strong and rich—what's her reason?
Why won't mother let me love him?
I'd have boots, a carriage too!
Why won't mother let me love him?
I'd have boots, a carriage too!

Wed a poor man—what befalls you?
Scanty food, scanty clothing.
Well, they say what can't be, can't be.
Now I'm doomed to live alone.
Well, they say what can't be, can't be.
Now I'm doomed to live alone.

Kolib mati ne byla,
Tob ja lykho robyla:
Čerez horu ta v kontoru
Do pysarja khodyla,
Čerez horu ta v kontoru
Do pysarja khodyla.

One Is High and One Is Low

One is high and one is low, yet both are moun-tains, broth-er.

I have one girl here at home, and, far a-way, an-oth-er.

For your deep black eye-brows I have loved you since I met you.

Though I can't be with you, dar-ling, Nev-er shall my heart for-get you.

Here at home my sweetheart has fine cows and land and riches.
But my sweetheart far away with eyebrows black bewitches.
For your deep black eyebrows
I have loved you since I met you.
Though I can't be with you, darling,
Never shall my heart forget you.

Anyone who wants to take my girl at home, may have her.
No one else can have the other, I'll keep *her* forever.
For your deep black eyebrows
I have loved you since I met you.
Though I can't be with you, darling,
Never shall my heart forget you.

Odna hora vysokaja, a druhaja nyzka.
Odna myla dalekaja, a druhaja blyzka!
On tak, moja myla,
Kokhanaja, čornobryva,
Khot' z toboju žyt' ne budu,
po vik serce, ne zabudu!

Cossack's Farewell

Take me to the Dis - tant Coun - try!" Coun - try!"

"Tell me, tell me, sweetheart,
What will you be doing,
When you're in the Distant Country?"
"I'll work there. I'll do washing,
Cut the grain in time of harvest,
When I'm in the Distant Country."

"Tell me, tell me, sweetheart,
What will you be eating,
When you're in the Distant Country?"
"Enough are bread and water
When I'm with you, Cossack hero,
With you in the Distant Country."

"Tell me, tell me, sweetheart,
Where will you be sleeping,
When you're in the Distant Country?"
"Enough are barns and haycocks,
When I'm with you, Cossack hero,
With you in the Distant Country."

Kozak odjiždaje,
Divčynon'ka plače:
Kudy jideš, kozače?
Kozače—sobolju,
Viz'my mene iz soboju
Na vkrajinu daleku!

Divčynon'ko myla,
Ščo ž budeš robyti
Na vkrajini dalekij?
Budu khusti prati,
Zelenogo žyta žati
Na vkrajini dalekij!

Divčynon'ko myla,
Ščo ž budeš ty jisti
Na vkrajini dalekij?
Sukhari z vodoju,
Aby, serce, iz toboju
Na vkrajini dalekij!

Divčynon'ko myla,
De ž budeš ti spati
Na vkrajini dalekij?
V stepu, pid verboju,
Aby, serce, iz toboju
Na vkrajini dalekij!

You Are a Bride

"Charms I had woven, woven of flowers.
At my white face he'd gaze for long hours.
One day he spoke it, 'Be you my bride, dear,
I'll be your husband, live by your side, dear'.

"No sooner made his promise, than broken,
All, all forgotten, what he had spoken.
If I am woeful, woeful he made me.
All the world hear me: He has betrayed me!

"One man I cherished, him whom I knew not.
One man I've married, him whom I love not.
Yes, I'm a bride and brides should look joyful.
Bride and betrayed, I can but be woeful."

Oj, ty, divčyno zaručenaja,
Čoho ž ty khodyš zasmučenaja?
Oj, khožu, khožu zasmučenaja,
Ščo ne za tebe zaručenaja!

Oj, ty, divčyno, slovami bluďyš,
Sama ne znaješ, koho ty ljubiš!
Oj, znaju, znaju, koho kokhaju,
Til'ky ne znaju, z kym žyty maju!

Oj, znaju, znaju, iz kym kokhajus',
Til'ky ne znaju, z kym izvinčajus'.
Vyjduna pole, hljanu na more,
Sama ja baču, ščo meni hore.

Sama ja baču, čoho ja plaču
Svoho myloho v viči ne baču.
Budu stojati ne tim kameni,
Poky ne pryjde mylyj do mene!

Polish

ONE INEVITABLY THINKS of Poland in terms of its tragic history. The destruction of the country by the Nazis in 1939 was unspeakably cruel, but it has parallels again and again in recent centuries. In the eighteenth century Poland was a puppet in the hands of Frederick the Great of Prussia, Queen Catherine of Russia, and the Austrian Maria Theresa. Poland's normal role was that of a buffer state, but these ambitious and unscrupulous rulers constantly laid designs against some part of the little kingdom, in the interest of some new interpretation of the balance of power. The familiar Hitlerian trick of the mutual assistance pact was frequently invoked by the Emperors, but

when the Poles raised an army to protect themselves from the attacks of one power they could seldom count on any real assistance from their neighbors. Once a land grab was conceived, all three powers usually claimed some share of the booty. And thus, after three "partitionings" the Polish nation disappeared in 1795, not to be reborn until after the First World War. Time and again there seemed to be faint hopes of a rebirth of the kingdom—when Napoleon "rescued" the Austrian and Prussian sections, for instance; but the glowering of the three powers, or of any one of them, was enough to keep a new Poland from arising. Both the Germans and the Russians made intensive efforts to wipe out any sense of a national past among the Poles: the native language was not taught in schools, history was distortedly rewritten to provide a *coup de grace* to national pride, and gaudy promises of autonomy were in fact ignored.

These are broad generalizations, imperfectly suggesting the Polish interest in a unity of its peoples, scarcely hinting at the internal difficulties that arose from frightful class inequality and ignorance. But we can see clearly that international political immorality subjected the Poles for generations to the same kind of autocratic and despotic rule that was the lot of all the small kingdoms and minority racial groups in Europe.

Poland was at the crossroads between western and eastern Europe, and therefore absorbed the songs of her neighbors—the Russians, the Germans, the Czechs and Slovaks—and in turn spread her own musical wares, especially eastward. The fame of Polish folk music was indeed so great that one of Bach's German contemporaries, Georg Philipp Telemann, could declare in the eighteenth century that "a Polish song makes the whole world dance."

It used to be said of the aged folk singers who traveled from village to village chanting their ballads and lyrics: "They are men who remember old songs and better times." There exist a few historical and legendary ballads that take us back to those early days when Polish borderers were busy fighting the Turk on their southern frontiers. But for the most part, the Polish genius has been lyrical. As in most of the other eastern European countries, there are a large number of pieces related to special festivals. Marriage was the most important family celebration, and each of the steps in a ceremonial peasant wedding had its own song to accompany the conventionalized drama. There are songs for the placing of the bride's cap, for the bride's departure from her parents,

for the procession of the bride and bridesmaids to the marriage chamber, for the couple's departure to the groom's home. There are special songs for Christmas, called *koleda* (cf. the Rumanian *colinde*), songs for Easter, for the beginning of spring, for the summer solstice, for the harvest, and so on through the peasant's year.

In addition to songs for special occasions, there are the usual occupational songs to be found in every folk literature—songs of boatmen, shepherds, beggars, soldiers, and the like—and pieces about domestic life, in which the Poles introduced very little novelty into the old subjects of married life, the mother-in-law, the wayward husband and the overworked wife. The Poles have, however, made a real contribution in their humorous and satiric songs. These usually take the form of "razzing" people from some other district. The peoples of the Masuren and Kujawiak districts in northwest Poland, and the inhabitants of the southern mountains have, since the sixteenth century, carried on what one authority has called a song warfare. Quite naturally they satirized foreigners among whom they moved. The Ruthenians, the Germans and the Jews especially were subjected to good-natured ridicule.

Fully half the prodigious number of extant Polish folksongs concern love. When one has made even a cursory study of this class of song it is quite obvious that the music is far superior to the poetry. Any poet, lettered or unlettered, faces difficulties when he attempts to speak freshly about the oldest and least conversational of the emotions. The chief difficulty in Poland seems, however, to be of a different sort. Dr. Paul Eisner, who has made a special study of the literary background of Slavic folk poetry, believes that Polish folk art has been penalized by the early cultural progress in the country. More than any of the other Slavic groups, he says, Poland was acquainted with

Western literary movements, and he attributes the chief harmful influences to the prominent school of seventeenth-century poetry. Whereas the dominant folk idiom had been primitive simplicity, it became consciously imitative and lost its fine—and essential—spontaneity. This is an interesting theory, not to be followed too far, but probably accurate in explaining the particular character of Polish love lyrics.

As to the music itself, most of the folk melodies seem Western in tone. The contrast between Russian and Polish musical idioms is the contrast between eastern and western Slavic peoples. The infrequency with which we meet modal tunes suggests not only that few of our tunes are old; it also implies the influence of Western, particularly German, musical ideas. One occasionally does meet unequal phrases in songs. Our "Rosemary, Lovely Garland" and "Stands a Maple," for example, are not constructed on the usual four-measure pattern, but begin and end with three-measure phrases. Triple time is a favorite of the Poles and is to be found in six of our eight examples.

Although they are not represented in this collection, the Polish dancing songs must be mentioned. Because of the popularity of Chopin, the Polish national character seems to the outside world to be summed up in the rhythms of his polonaises and mazurkas. But without wishing to comment upon Chopin's artistry, we must point out that he did not imbibe his fervent patriotism from the folk. He learned the national dances from playing in Warsaw salons when he was young. And what he has given the world in his fifty-two mazurkas and twelve polonaises bears slight relation to the airs familiar to folk dancers. Rather, Chopin has used his raw material freely to develop his own artistic product. Of the mazurka, W. Barclay Squire in *Grove's Dictionary* says, "He extended its original forms, eliminated all vulgarity, introduced all sorts of

Polish airs, and thus retained little more than the intensely national character of the original simple dance tune." This statement is relatively true of his handling of the polonaise.

Chopin's inventiveness aside, the Poles did express themselves uniquely in their folk dances. The mazurka was a dance in triple time for four or eight couples. The accepted methods of executing the dance left enough liberty for creation to make the dance largely improvisational. By the middle of the nineteenth century a somewhat chastened form of the mazurka had swept westward as far as England, captivating Berlin, Paris and London as it went. The krakowiak (cracovienne), which originated in Krakow, the ancient capital, is a dance in duple time, a kind of galop with much syncopation and many regional variations. Like the mazurka, these dances were accompanied by intermittent singing. The krakowiak, according to a nineteenth-century observer, is usually punctuated by the improvised couplet or quatrain of one dancer, capped by another from someone else who takes up the idea and adds a fresh twist—whether it be a satiric or amorous description of someone present or a comment about politics.

The polonaise was not of popular origin, but the people eventually took over a version of this slow march-like processional whose rhythm is like that of the Spanish bolero.

These are but three of the large number of national dances; many more are regional in extent, such as those of the southern mountain Poles, who are strongly influenced by the Slovaks nearby. One must remember that influential though the Polish folk song and dance have been on composers from Bach onward, we still need to return to the original folk melodies themselves to understand the real temper of the Polish people.

Of the eight Polish songs in our collection, seven are in minor keys. This proportion was probably not arrived at deliberately, but it may be justified. Certainly the sadness of the songs here is more genuine in its intensity than in most of the minor moods one encounters. A characteristic joyous mood is to be found in the dancing songs with their ordinarily brisk tempos and pronounced rhythms. But here we have a group of laments. The subject is everywhere love, and the lover is either simply unhappy or he is forsaken or dying. Even "Love Oracle," which describes the Silesian folk ritual of casting flowers upon the water as a love oracle, is in minor, and the end (fragmentary in our text) suggests that the swans are not able to avert an unhappy prophecy. The single song in major, "Stands a Maple," is a properly expectant evening song, though it ends quizzically.

"Yasha and Kasha" is a fragment of a very popular ballad. Oscar Kolberg in 1857 printed fifty-four versions of the piece, almost all of them sung to variants of a single melodic archetype in minor. Some of the variants are in major, while a few are based on modal scales. The song was popular in all Polish districts, but tunes most nearly like ours (which happens to be taken from a more recent collection) were sung in the district of Radom in central Poland. The ballad recounts a cruel story of betrayal and murder in which Yasha lures Kasha into the woods on the pretext of love, and then proceeds to rob her of her jewels and finery. Our fragment reveals this much of the story; but instead of Kasha's sad return, in the longer texts Yasha throws her into a stream and she drowns. Fishermen cast their nets and recover the body, which lies in state in the hallway of the house as the poem ends. There are, of course, many variants in details as this story was circulated over a wide area. The folk motifs here recall the American ballad "The Jealous Lover" and the Scots "Twa Sisters."

Boat, My Good Companion

Boat, my good com - pan - ion, now o - bey your mas - ter.

See the riv - er rush - ing: go you e - ven fast - er.

"Troub - led is the riv - er, ang - ry waves are snarl - ing.

You will nev - er see her, nev - er see your dar - ling."

Never see her, say you? I've no fear: we're going.
Since I was a baby I've been good at rowing.
Sooner will a maiden slight a faithful lover
Than a stormy river harm a sturdy rower.

Vistula, gray river, long we've been together,
Always I have loved you, never feared your weather.
Let me row in safety, though your waves are snarling:
I am in a hurry, I must see my darling.

"Stakh, poor little boatman, see your darling, say you?
Go and see the ocean—that will not betray you!
She is yours no longer—no more use in rowing.
Dancing at a wedding, that's what she is doing."

Boat, my good companion, though the waves are snarling,
Be yourself your steersman, seek no more my darling.
Gray and swirling river, take my oars and rudder,
For my love has left me, left me for another.

Łódko moja łódko suwaj po głębinie . . .
Płyńże chyżo, wartko, Jako woda płynie!
Porwie rwąca fala Rzuci na głębiny . . .
Nie dojedziesz Stachu do swojej dziewczyny!

Co niemam dojechać? przeciem w ręku krzepki . . .
Z wiosłem znam się dobrze niemal od kolebki! . . .
Prędzej zdradzi płocha dziewczyna chłopaka—
Niźli zdradzi fala chyżego flisaka! . . .

Hej! Wisełko szara! Hej! ty wodo rwąca! . . .
Razem myšmy razem prawie od miesiąca . . .
Nieš że mnie bezpiecznie przez wartkie głębiny
Bo mi już i spieszno do mojej dziewczyny.

Oj! Stachu! Stasieńku! Flisaku nieboże!
Prędzej ty zobaczysz dzisiaj modre morze,
Niż swoją dziewczynę! . . . Już ona nie twoja! . . .
Tańczy na weselu zdradliwa dziewoja!

Łódko moja łodko! Spiesz dalej a dalej . . .
Już mojej dziewczyny nie będziem szukali! . . .
Rzucam wiosła w wodę! Nieš że fało modra!
Kiedy mnie jedyna dziewczyna zawiodła! . . .

I Sowed Millet

I sowed mil - let in my mead - ow, mil - let nev - er got;

Loved a pret — ty girl and wooed her, but I won her not.

Sow-ing seed does not mean that you'll get grain. Lov-ing one does not mean a bride you'll gain.

So I do not blame my dar - ling, just my luck - less lot.

216

When the millet started growing, came the hail and cold.
So is love doomed in this world where hearts are bought and sold.
Came the hail, took away my hopes of grain.
Came the world, took the bride I hoped to gain.
Still I love her, think about her, in my heart her hold.

Proso zeszło, lecz przed żniwem zbił je zimny grad,
Moją miłość do dziewczyny, zły zepsowal świat,
Plon zboża zniszczył grad,
Dziewczęcia nie dał świat,
Choć zawiodła me nadzieje, wspominam ją rad.

Siałem proso na zagonie, nie mogłem go żąć.
Pokochałem lube dziewcze, nie mogłem jon wziąć.
Bo posiać, to nie żąć,
Bo kochać, to nie wziąć.
Choć mnie zdradza lube dziewczę, nie mogę jon kląć.

Yasha and Kasha

"Kasha, stop your crying; go and get some silver,
Get both gold and silver, all my horse can carry,
Get both gold and silver, all my horse can carry."

Now they're in the forest; now they leave the forest.
"Kasha, go back home now, go home to your father,
Kasha, go back home now, go home to your father."

Kasha turned and left him, walked back to the forest,
Stumbled through the forest, eyes half blind with weeping,
Stumbled through the forest, eyes half blind with weeping.

Jasio konie poił, Kasia wode brała,
Jasio sobie śpiewał, Kasia zapłakała,
Jasio sobie śpiewał Kasia zapłakała.

Nabierzże Kasieńko srebra złota dosyć,
Zeby miał mój konik co zsobą u nosić,
Zeby miał moj konik co zsobą u nosić.

Do boru wjechali, wyjechali z boru,
Wróćże się Kasieńko do swych ojców dworu,
Wróćże się Kasieńko do swych ojców dworu.

Przez lasy przez bory Kasieńka wracała,
Nim zaszła do domu, oczy wypłakała,
Nim zaszła do domu oczy wypłakała.

Rosemary, Lovely Garland

"Rather, why should I not fade? I am no longer untouched.
See how my leaves, once shining, see how my blooms, once lovely,
Fall now and lie in the dust."

Open, O hard flinty rock, so will my heart find its rest.
Break into fifty pieces, so my heart sorely troubled,
Troubled and breaking, will rest.

"Though I break open for you, open and open again,
Yet your heart, lovely maiden, your sad heart, lovely maiden,
Never again will find rest."

O jezioro, jezioro, bystra woda wtobie jest;
Wionku z maryjonku,
Wionku z maryjonku, na głowie mi więdnie jesz.

Jakżebym nie miał więdnieć, gdy już nie jestem cały,
Zielone listeczki, modre fijoleczki
Ze mnie już opadają.

O rozstąp się, kamieniu, ulżyj sercu mojemu,
Rozstąp się na dwoje, pociesz serce moje,
Ach bo jest zasmucone.

Choćbych ja się rozstąpił i na dziesięcioro,
To twoje serdeczko, nadobna dzieweczko,
Już nie będzie wesołe.

Stands a Maple

Groans he, wounded on the ground,
"Will you help me now, Kasha?
Help your Yasha now, Kasha,
Find a healing herb, cure my wound."

"Can help come to Yasha by me?"
"Yes, if you will go quickly,
To the forest go quickly,
Find the healing herb, rosemary."

Long she sought, at last found the herb.
Found it, homeward turned, running.
Now she hears a man running,
Coming through the wood, calling her.

"Kasha, drop the flower you have,
Drop the herb you have, Kasha.
Underneath the tree, Kasha,
They are digging Yasha a grave."

Stoi jawor zielony, stoi jawor zielony,
U mej matki rodzonej, u mej matki rodzonej,

Pod jaworem łożeńko, pod jaworem łożeńko,
Na niem leży Jasieńko. Na niem leży Jasieńko.

Leży, leży zraniony, leży, leży zraniony,
Woła Kasi strapionej: woła Kasi strapionej:

Moja Kasiu ratuj mnie, moja Kasiu ratuj mnie,
Szukaj ziółka, lekuj mnie. Szukaj ziółka, lekuj mnie.

Czemże mam cię ratować? Czemże mam cię ratować?
Jakiem ziołkiem lekować? Jakiem ziołkiem lekować?

Idź Kasieńku do gaju, idź Kasieńku do gaju,
Przynieś ziela rozmaju. Przynieś ziela rozmaju.

Jeszcze Kasia nie doszła, jeszcze Kasia nie doszła,
Już-ci za nią szlą posła: już-ci za nią szlą posła:

Wróć się Kasiu do domu, wróć się Kasiu do domu,
Prowadź Jasia do grobu. Prowadź Jasia do grobu.

Kasia ziele rzucila, Kasia ziele rzuciła,
Za głowke się chwyciła: za głowke się chwyciła:

Nieszczęśliwa godzina, nieszczęśliwa godzina,
Żem przy śmierci nie była. Żem przy śmierci nie była.

O mój Boże kochany, o mój Boże kochany,
Wziąłeś mi kwiat różany; wziąłeś mi kwiat różany;

O mój Boże jedyny, o mój Boże jedyny,
Wziales mi kwiat lilii! Wziales mi kwiat lilii!

Mój Jasieńku klejnocie, mój Jasieńku klejnocie,
Chodziłam ja we złocie: chodziłam ja we złocie:

A teraz ja po tobie, a teraz ja po tobie,
Chodzić będę w załobie. Chodzić będę w załobie.

Do południa w żalobie, do południa w żalobie,
Po poludniu tak sobie; po poludniu tak sobie;

Dniem żałobę uświęcę, dniem żałobę uświęcę,
Nocka w tanku wykrece. Nocka w tanku wykrece.

Bo żałoba na tydzień, bo żałoba na tydzień,
Zalotnicy w każdy dzień; zalotnicy w każdy dzien;

Więc ze smutku wielkiego, więc ze smutku wielkiego,
Wyjść muszę za innego. Wyjść muszę za innego.

Wind of Night

There's my love coming, ah, how my heart's drumming!
His fastest horse riding, his horse so proudly striding!
Love me each hour, with all your heart's power.
If me you so cherish, I'll love you till I perish.

See, a hind drinking, her muzzle deep sinking.
Oh, this believe, true-love, ne'er will I change for new love.
Deep the hind's drinking, so deep my mind's thinking:
If you will not save me, then let the churchyard have me!

Leci głos po rosie prosto ku trachtowi:
Powiedz dobry wieczór memu kochankowi,
Powiedz dobry wieczór, kłaniaj się odemnie:
Żeli ón mnie kocha, ja jego wzajemnie.

Widzę ja zdaleka siwego konika,
Kochanek moj jedzie, serce mi przenika.
A gdy podłańczuku, a gdy serce czuje,
Będę cię kochała, puko tylko żyję.

Przy bystrym jeziorze wileń wodę pije:
Pamiętaj, pamiętaj, ja dla ciebie żyję.
Ja dla ciebie żyję, dla ciebie umieram,
Dla cię świat zamykam, grób sobie otwieram.

You Could See My Faith

Yet the fault is mine, yet the fault is mine,
For I knew not how to keep from sight
All my love for you, all my love for you,
When I knew you but in dreams at night.

I remember well, I remember well,
Cherish still the words you spoke to me.
Whether I did dream, whether I did wake,
You were with me, never left me free.

Tell your new love now, tell your new love now,
You have never loved a girl before.
Fold your hands and swear, fold your hands and swear,
As to me but yesterday you swore.

Ty co w stałość moję wierzysz.
Coś dał probę tyranii,
Ztwą miłością ku mnię spieszysz,
A twa zdrada mię rani.

Jam to winna, żem ci dała,
Poznać ogień mój wcześnie,
O miłościm powiedziała,
Tak cię znając jak we snie.

Z radością tom spominała,
Co twe usta mówiły,
Spiąc, czuwając tom myślała . . .
Twe mię wdzięki zgubiły.

Teraz innéj tak powiadaj,
Zem się nie znała z tobą;
Przysięgaj się, ręce składaj,
Jak mnieś czynił przed dobą.

Ciesz się, podły niewdzięczniku,
Żeś zwyciężył niewinną;
Tych sposobów okrutniku,
Używasz już nad inną.

Rozpacz mi się zemścić każe,
Lecz ja myślę rozumnie,
Dość gdy cię z serca wymażę . . .
Nie kochanyś już u mnie.

Love Oracle

"Why are you crying, why, pretty maiden, what has befallen you, say?
Is it for Yasha? Then stop your crying, he will be with you this day."

"Yasha, my true-love, true-love mine Yasha, full is my heart of dismay.
Crowns I have woven, thrown in the water—see, they are floating away."

"Kasha, my true-love, true-love mine Kasha, smile then, away with these
        frowns!
Three swans I cherish, white as white lilies, they shall swim after your
        crowns.

"Hurry, swans, hurry, leave her not hopeless, none else can answer her
        prayer."
Not one crown bring they, only a flower—Kasha, put that in your hair!"

W polu lipeńka, w polu zielona, listeczki opusciła.
Podnią dziewczyna, pod nią jedyna parę wianuszków wiła.

Oj czego płaczesz moja dziewczyno, ach cóż ci za niedola?
Oj nie płacz Kasiu, smutnaś po Jasiu, ach będziesz ci go miała.

O mój Jaieńku, o mój jedyny, da stałać mi się szkoda,
Uwiłam ci ja parę wianuszków, zabrała mi je woda.

Moja dziewczyno, moja jedyna, nie kłopocz ty się o nie,
Oj mam ja parę białych łabędzi, popłynąć one po nie.

Już jeden płynie, po rokicinie, goni za wiankiem strzałą,
Już drugi płynie, aż się odhynie, ale z pociechą małą.

Łabędzie płyną, wianeczki toną, bystra je woda garnie,
Moje wianeczki z drobnej ruteczki, mamli was stracić marnie?

Łabędzie płyną, wianeczki giną, bystra je woda niesię,
Nie masz wianeczka, moja dzieweczka, już ja cię nie pocieszę.

Łabędzie wróćcie, serca nie smućcie, wianeczka nie przyniosły,
Tylko rąbeczek, to na czepeczek, na twoje złote włosy.

Wendish

IN SOUTHEASTERN GERMANY, between Dresden and Breslau, is a small district of about 200,000 persons who speak a West Slavic dialect. This "linguistic island," entirely surrounded by German influences, comprises the old provinces of Upper and Lower Lusatia. The people call themselves Serbs or Sorbs or Lužičane; the Germans call them Wends, from an old word formerly applied to Slavs generally. This interesting little region has inevitably been dominated by German ideas and institutions. The German language has threatened the extinction of the Wendish. From almost every point of view this cell of alien language and culture seems too small to fight for its life.

The Wends have left no real literary mark on the world, for quite obvious reasons. But their folk songs have always been well-known, and constitute the only cultural exportation to the outside world. In 1836 one of the Wendish literary societies was farsighted enough to realize that these treasures should be gathered before their richness began to dwindle, and accordingly offered a prize for the best collection of Wendish folksongs. Four contestants came forward, and though none of them qualified for the prize, out of their initial efforts grew a splendid work edited by J. L. Haupt and J. E. Schmaler.[1] It contains some 500 songs and is the storehouse of information on the customs and folklore of the Wendish people.

Throughout this work the overpowering influence of Germany is evident. Most of the songs had been compiled by a young Wendish theologian named Smoler, but by the time the book was published he had a German collaborator and the spelling of his own name was Germanized. It is clear that by the 1840's the

national dance was meeting strong competition from the waltzes, galops and schottisches popular in central Europe. The common native instruments, the *husla* (a three-stringed fiddle), the *tarawaka* (a kind of oboe) and the bagpipe, were being superseded by the modern German village orchestra of strings, clarinets and horns. Among the songs in the Haupt-Schmaler volume there are at least fifty German ballads.

Yet it would be unfair to say that Wendish folk music does not have its individuality. Although it is possible to date only a few of the historical pieces, some of the melodies are in the old ecclesiastical modes—usually a sign of considerable age. And there are a large number of three-part tunes, set to couplets, one line of which is repeated in each stanza. With the exception of dancing songs most of the melodies are sung slowly, ornamented frequently with trills and tremolos. As in the performance of some Cossack songs of the Eastern Slavs, one stanza is connected to the next by the singer's soaring from the concluding note to the fifth or octave above, then settling to the opening note of the next stanza.

Linguistically the Wendish dialect forms a transition between Czech and Polish, and Wendish folksong is likewise essentially West Slavic, despite the strong impress of German form and subject-matter. Our three Wendish songs are relatively modern, and are typical of the native dance music. "Hanka" is in the style of a Polish mazurka. The few embellishments in the original printed versions (and not included here) did not interfere with the strong rhythmic character of the melodies. The national dance, resembling alike the polonaise and the minuet, was performed to a large number of melodies.

---

[1] *Volkslieder der Wenden in der Ober- und Nieder-Lausitz* (Grimma, 1841-3).

Good Night

Sweetheart mine, good night, dearest love, good night!
Happy be your dreams, my own true love.
Sweetheart mine, good night, dearest love, good night!
Happy be your dreams, my own true love.
Churchward we'll soon be walking, then they will stop their talking.
Happy be your dreams, my own true love.
Churchward we'll soon be walking, then they will stop their talking.
Happy be your dreams, my own true love.
Happy be your dreams, my own true love.

Měj ty dobru nóc, měj ty dobru nóc,
Och ty moja luba lubčička!
Měj ty dobru nóc, měj ty dobru nóc,
Och ty moja luba lubčička!
Za to lubowanje, za to šwarkotanje,
Och ty moja luba lubčička!
Za to lubowanje, za to šwarkotanje,
Och ty moja luba lubčička,
Och ty moja luba lubčička!

Měj ty dobru nóc, měj ty dobru nóc,
Och ty moja luba lubčička!
Měj ty dobru nóc, měj ty dobru nóc,
Och ty moja luba lubčička!
Dyrbju dom ňet króčić, chcu so zasowróćić,
Och ty moja luba lubčička!
Dyrbju dom ňet króčić, chcu so zasowróćić,
Och ty moja luba lubčička,
Och ty moja luba lubčička!

Vain Serenade

Your poor Yan-ek's heart is break – ing. Find some way to
me to creep, now your moth – er's fast a – sleep."

"Do you think my mother rules me? drumdi, drumdi, tralala.
Only one thing she forbids me, drumdi, drumdi, tralala,
I may love just whom I want to, only one thing that I can't do:
Never leave your room, she said, when the sun has gone to bed."

"Hanka, don't let that disturb you, drumdi, drumdi, tralala,
Even now the sun is rising, drumdi, drumdi, tralala.
I must see you, I must kiss you, you don't know how much I miss you!
Find some way to me to creep, now your mother's fast asleep."

"Who told *you* my mother's sleeping? drumdi, drumdi, tralala.
She's not here, she's gone out dancing, drumdi, drumdi, tralala.
Now it's really light. I wonder who's that woman coming yonder?
Bless me, it's my mother! Quick!
Yanek, better run or you will taste her stick!"

Běžał hólčik pře wšě hórki, drumdi, drumdi, tralala!
Wował holčcy do komorki, drumdi, drumdi, tralala!
Spišliabo njespiš, Hanka? Wusłyš, miłe, swojoh Janka!
Pój, pój ke mni z komorki, njeprašej so, njeprašej so maćeŕki!

Přečo bych so njeprašała, drumdi, drumdi, tralala!
Mać mi njeje zakazała, drumdi, drumdi, tralala!
Zo bych hólca lubowała. Jeno to je zakazała:
Njekhodź, njekhodź z komorki, hdyž so ćmowje, hdyž so ćmowje wjećori!

Hanka luba, to je krasnje, drumdi, drumdi, tralala!
Dźensa ćma njej, je tak jasnje! Drumdi, drumdi, tralala!
Pój won, słyšmje, ja će pošu, njech so z tobu horco košu!
Wustuṕ, wustuṕ z komorki, njewubudź pak, njewubudź pak maćeŕki!

Njewubudźu, dźens sym sama, drumdi, drumdi, tralala!
Na bjesadu šła je mama! Drumdi, drumdi, tralala!
Krasnje, Janko, ćmu ja hidźu, jasnje pak tež hižo widźu,
Naša mać dźe z přazy dom: Janko, zmiń so, Janko, zmiń so z wětřikom!

Hanka

Hanka, with lips so rosy red, oh, how I love to watch you!
Hanka, with lips so rosy red, oh, how I love to watch you!
There you stand, I see you now.
You smile at me—pearls your teeth when you smile.
There you stand, I see you now.
You smile at me—pearls your teeth when you smile.

Hanka, with feet as white as milk, oh, how I love to watch you!
There you stand, I see you now.
Stop standing there! Come and help lift this pail!
There you stand, I see you now.
Stop standing there! Come and help lift this pail!

Hanka, ty brune, brune wóčko, ja će derje widźu,
Hanka, ty brune, brune wóčko, ja će derje widźu!
We tej hustej šmrjokowincy, na tom zelenem kopičku,
We tej hustej šmrjokowincy, na tom zelenem kopičku! [Hahej!]

Hanka, ty módra, módra hubka, ja će derje widźu,
Hanka, ty módra, módra hubka, ja će derje widźu!
Wosrjedź hubki běłe zubki, lubje na mnje so posměwaš!
Wosrjedź hubki běłe zubki, lubje na mnje so posměwaš! [Hahej!]

Hanka, ty běła, běła nóžka, ja će derje widźu,
Hanka, ty běła, běła nóžka, ja će derje widźu!
Pohoń lóžku běłu nóžku, pomhaj mi ćežki karan njesć!
Pohoń lóžku běłu nóžku, pomhaj mi ćežki karan njesć! [Hahej!]

Yiddish

IN THE FOURTEENTH century King Casimir the Great of Poland invited a large number of Jews from the Rhine valley to swell the population of cities in his country. Thus was begun an important migration of this constantly harassed people, who settled not only in Poland but also in southern and western Russia and in the old Kingdom of Lithuania. For a time the Low German language they brought with them continued to develop along with the parent stem. But eventually contact was virtually broken off with the German Jews, and the language of the Jewish communities in Eastern Europe went its divergent way, developing slightly different dialects in each of the three countries where the Jews had been

repatriated. This is the language called Yiddish (from the German *Jüdisch*), written in Hebrew characters, and thus a private language of the Jews. The periodic repressions and pogroms have perhaps enhanced the tenacity of this quasi-international language among its speakers.

The German core of the speech has been enriched by many Hebrew and Aramaic words from the Bible and the Talmud and the ecclesiastical ritual. The Jews' business associations in the new countries inevitably brought a Slavic element into Yiddish, especially during the second half of the nineteenth century.

Like the language, the folklore of the Eastern Jews has been the product of both religious and secular influences. Jewish folk-tales range the world in subject-matter, drawing from sources such as the Talmud, the Arabian Nights, the legends of King Arthur, the adventures of Sinbad the Sailor, and weaving stories from widely dispersed elements. A good yarn may travel faster and further than a folksong, but in music too the Eastern Jews have assimilated freely. Their folksongs include many adaptations of Lithuanian and Polish, and, more recently, Ukrainian melodies. Tunes from the Rumanians and the South Slavs find their way in. The air of the Slovakian National Anthem (our "Let Me Keep Faith"), which we know was popular also in Hungary, turns up in modified form as a Yiddish folk melody. As is ordinarily the case with migratory tunes, a domesticating process has usually affected the music of foreign origin.

The Yiddish muse is preeminently lyrical. Aside from the religious recitativos which derive from ecclesiastical music, the songs are largely domestic lyrics: cradle lullabies, songs of childhood, love and marriage, complaints, songs of oppression and death, and—by no means least—humorous and satiric songs. "In the folksong of the Eastern Jew," says Idelsohn, "the soul of the Jewish masses has again, after long centuries, found its expression. In these songs the soul of the folk runs the whole gamut of feeling; all social strata have their voice, from highest to lowest, from Rabbi and Talmud scholar to thief, from mother to prostitute. The folksong is a faithful expression of the life of the Jewish people in Eastern Europe." [1]

---

[1] A. Z. Idelsohn, *Der Volkgesang der Osteuropäischen Juden* (Leipzig, 1932), p. vii.

The minor mode predominates in the music, but this is not, says Idelsohn, to be interpreted as a sign of pathos or resignation. In his collection of some seven hundred melodies, only one-tenth are in major, and he points out that an almost similar fondness for minor or modal scales is to be found wherever there is a strong Oriental influence—in the songs of modern Greece or of ancient Spain, for example. And in these countries, as in Czechoslovakia and Hungary, many humorous songs and lively dances are found in minor. It is clear that Western ideas about the emotional values of major and minor keys cannot be applied loosely to the music of the East.

With the emigration of Eastern Jews to America, the Yiddish folksong has been transplanted to our shores. Many of the most important collections have been published in New York during this century, and with the presence of many Yiddish newspapers in our large cities, the language and the folk traditions are gaining today an unexpected encouragement.

Of our six songs, one is a berceuse, or lullaby, three are concerned with love, and two ("Girls of Today" and "The Poor Aunt") are wedding-party songs of contrasting moods. "What Maidens Want," with its reference to the marriage-broker, recalls an old Orthodox Jewish custom of parental negotiation for the spouse of son or daughter. Many unhappy weddings resulted from loveless matches, many a grass-widow was left behind when life became too unattractive for the husband; but the young girl in our song is oblivious of any misfortune that may lie in store for her. The text, which has been set to music by Brahms, was originally a low German folk-poem, "Och, modder, ick will en ding haben."

What Maidens Want

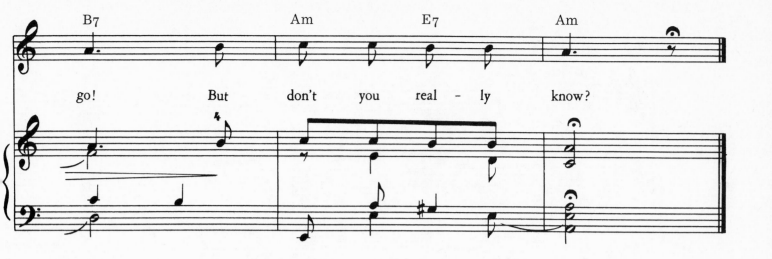

"Mother, mother, come sing a song for me, tell me *what* maidens want!"
"It's ear-rings they want to have, pretty gold ear-rings;
Let's go now and speak to the goldsmith."
"No, mother mine, no! Those too I can forego. But don't you really
    know?

"Mother, mother, come sing a song for me, tell me *what* maidens want!"
"It's hats that they want to have, hats bright with flowers;
Let's go now and speak to the milliner."
"No, mother mine, no! Hats too I can forego. But don't you really
    know?

"Mother, mother, come sing a song for me, tell me *what* maidens want!"
"It's bridegrooms they want to have, young, rich, and handsome;
Let's go now and speak to the broker."
"Yes, mother mine, yes! You've made a lucky guess! That's it, I must
    confess!"

Yohmeh, yohmeh, shpil nohr a liedeleh, vos doss maideleh vil?
Doss maideleh vil a pohr shichelech hohben.
Muz mehn gein dem shuhster zohgehn!
—Nein, Mamehschi, nein! Du kehnst mich nish fahrshtein!
    Du veihst nish vos ich mein!

Yohmeh, yohmeh, shpil nohr a liedeleh, vos doss maideleh vil?
Doss maideleh vil a hitteleh hohben,
Muz mehn gein dehr puhtzehrkeh zohgen!
—Nein, Mamehschi, nein! Du kehnst mich nish fahrshtein!
    Du kehnst nish vos ich mein!

Yohmeh, yohmeh, shpil nohr a liedeleh, vos doss maideleh vil?
Doss maideleh vil a pohr oyringlech hohben,
Muz mehn gein dem goldschmid zohgen!
—Nein, Mamehschi, nein! Du kehnst mich nish fahrshtein!
    Du veihst nish vos ich mein!

Yohmeh, yohmen, shpil nohr a liedeleh, vos doss maideleh vil?
Doss maideleh vil a chohsendel hohben,
Muz mehn gein dem shadchan zohgen!
—Yoh, Mamehschi, yoh! Du kehnst mich schoin fahrshtein!
    Du veihst schoin vos ich mein.

Girls of Today

"Play a tune for me, and play it nicely,
I will give you pennies three for playing.
Pennies three—that is really quite enough.
Play all night until the sky is graying."

"All night long is long enough, my lady.
Men are fools, they say—are women witty?
Call the tune—any tune you want to hear.
At your service! You are really pretty!"

Heintihkeh maidelech, die fahnfehrahnkess,
Zay gein oyf chahsehness uhn tahntsehn pohlkess,
Pohlkeh mahzur iz zeyehr leben,
Zey hohben kein grohschen dem klezmer tsu gehben.

Klezmer, klezmer, shpil mir schein,
'Ch' vel eich gehben ah dreihehr mein;
Ah dreihehr mein iz gohr kein sahch,
Ihr zohlt mir shpilehn ah gahntseh nahcht!

Ah gahntseh nahcht iz kein sahkohneh,
Meh tohr nisht chahseneh hohben mit ahn ahlmohneh,
Ahn ahlmohneh hoht kahlteh fiess—
Ah shein maideleh iz tsuhker-ziess.

The Poor Aunt

Chazkele, Chazkele, play a Russian dance for me.
I am poor, but I'm a pious woman.
Well, I know I'm poor, well I know I'm poor,
That's no reason my own blood should turn me from the door.

Nobody asked me here, I have come all by myself.
I am poor, but I'm your mother's sister.
Well I know I'm poor, well I know I'm poor,
That's no reason my own blood should turn me from the door.

Chatzkeleh, Chatzkeleh! Shpil mir ah kazahtzkeleh!
Chotsch ahn ohrehmeh, ahbi ah chwahtzkeh!
Ohrehm iz nit guht, ohrehm iz nit guht.
Lohmir zich nit shehmehn mit eigehneh bluht!

Chatzkeleh, Chatzkeleh! shpil-zeh mir ah duhmeh!
Chotsch ahn ohrehmeh, ahbi ah fruhmeh!
Ohrehm iz nit guht, ohrehm iz nit guht.
Lohmir zich nit shehmehn mit eigehneh bluht!

Chatzkeleh, Chatzkeleh, Shpil-zeh mir ah zehmeleh!
Chanehlehs chohseleh ruhft mehn Ahvrehmeleh.
Ohrehm iz nit guht, ohrehm iz nit guht.
Lohmir zich nit shehmehn mit eigehneh bluht!

Nit kain gebehteneh, ahlein gekuhmen!
Chotsch ahn ohrehmihnkeh, fohrt ah muhmeh!
Ohrehm iz nit guht, ohrehm is nit guht.
Lohmir zich nit shehmehn mit eigehneh bluht.

The Tailor Boy

Feel my heart's bit – ter ach – ing.

D.C. 𝄆

Twigs push out on the tree in the forest,
Twigs push out and the leaves grow green,
Twigs push out and the leaves grow green,
Seeing the green leaves, I, the poor tailor-boy,
Dream all day of my sweetheart.

Birds alight on the tree in the forest,
Birds alight and I hear them sing,
Birds alight and I hear them sing,
Hearing them singing, I, the poor tailor-boy,
Hear my heart's bitter moaning.

Tief in vehldeleh shteiht a baimeleh,
Uhn di tsveigehlech bliehn.
Uhn di tsveigehlech bliehm.
Uhn bei mir, ohrehm schneidehrel,
Mit mein hehrtzeleh tsiehn.

Oihfehn baimeleh vahgst ah tsveigeleh
Uhn di blehtelech tsvietehn;
Uhn di blehtelech tsvietehn;
Uhn mein ohrehm schvahcheh hehrtzeleh
Tsieht tsu mein ziesehr ietehn.

Oihfehn tsveigeleh shteiht ah faigeleh,
Uhn doss faigeleh pieschtscheht.
Uhn doss faigeleh pieschtscheht.
Uhn bei mir, ohrehm schneidehrel,
Mein schvach hehrtzeleh trieschtscheht.

Lullaby

248

Spirits sleeping fly to heaven, tell their sins in heaven,
But my sinless pretty baby sleeping has nothing to fear.
Lullaby my pretty baby, lullaby my dear.

Stop your crying, precious jewel, mother's oh so weary,
Sad your mother, sad and weary—sleep baby, mother is here.
Lullaby my pretty baby, lullaby my dear.

Shlohf, mein tohchtehr, sheineh, fieneh, ihn dein viegehleh.
'Ch' vehl zich zehtsehn lehbehn dir
Uhn zingehn ah liedeleh,
'Ch' vehl dich viegehn, liedehr zingehn,
Lulinkeh, mein kind.

Ihn shlohfehn geiht di nischohmeh ahroyhf uhn shreibt di ahveiruss ihn di bichehr,
Uhn du, mein kind, hohst noch kein zind
Kehnst shlohfehn ruik uhn zichehr.
Luleh, luleh, shlohf, mein gduhleh,
Lulinkeh, mein kind.

Pieschtschehst zich uhn veihnst uhn veihnst uhn shlohfehn vilstu nit,
Mahchst doch ohn dein ohrmeh muhtehr
Shmehrtsehn mit dehrmit.
Luleh, luleh, shlohf, mein gduhleh,
Lulinkeh, mein kind.

By Our Cottage

Ah, his lovely eyes of blue, eyes of blue!
Winter gone but newly, gone dark winter newly,

Thought I he spoke truly, thought I he spoke truly.
Winter gone but newly, thought I he spoke truly.

Bei mein mahmess heizeleh, heizeleh,
Bin ich mir gehshtahnen;
Ach, mein teiehr leben iz fahrbei gehgahngen,
Ach, mein teiehr leben iz fahrbei gehgahngen.

Mit die blaueh aigelech, aigelech,
Mit die blahndeh hohr;
'Ch'hohb gehmaint, ahz vos ehr rehdt iz doch ahltz vohr,
'Ch'hohb gehmaint, ahz vos ehr rehdt iz doch ahltz vohr.

'Ch'hohb gehmaint oyf zeineh raihd, oyf zeineh raihd
Kehn mehn shtehlen moyerhn.
Ez hoht dech mir ahzoinss gehtuhn,
Ahz ich muz nohr veihnen ihn troyehrn.

Ach, vey, Mameschi, Mameschi,
Mameschi ich fahl!
Zint 'ch'hohb ohngeh-hoybehn ah liebeh fihren,
Plahtst ihn mir die gahl, plahtst ihn mir die gahl.

Czechoslovakian

BOHEMIA, MORAVIA and Slovakia have had much in common for centuries. But only after the First World War did they realize their long desire for political independence. For a thousand years, the Slovaks were under Hungarian control; from 1526 to 1918 the Czechs of Bohemia and Moravia were subjects of the Austrian Hapsburg dynasty. In each kingdom the harsh rule ground peasants under a ruthless feudal system, suppressed civil liberties and independence of thought, and discouraged any sort of national awakening.

Though the three provinces were all nominally part of the Austro-Hungarian Empire during much of this time, their common western Slavic inheritance was subjected to severe strain. Austria tried desperately to Germanize all her miscellaneous and heterogeneous provinces, including Bohemia and Moravia. For a time the Czech language was seriously threatened: official business was conducted only in German, and the Teutons made it a point of pride not to learn Czech. The western borders were overrun by Germans who industrialized the region and in many respects westernized it—a fact of considerable importance in the development also of its folklore. Austria refused to consider any kind of federal union which would have allowed for the independent development of the component states, yet from the end of the eighteenth century, the Czech national spirit grew. An active literary movement took root; Dvořák and Smetana spread the musical fame of the Czechs round the world; and the cry for political autonomy was redoubled. Once the First World War had begun, Masaryk and Beneš went abroad to lay plans for a new West Slavic state, while at home the brave and valiant Czechs organized an underground movement comparable in its audacity and stubbornness only to that of the Second World War.

In contrast to the thickly populated and highly industrialized Czech regions, Slovakia has been a primitive agricultural state, thinly populated, connected with the outside world chiefly through the Danubian exit to the south. Because it is not rich or populous or easily accessible, its progress has been retarded. As one works eastward across Czechoslovakia, the domestic architecture becomes noticeably more primitive, illiteracy increases, and Western influences cease altogether. The strong Hungarian minority has been sizable enough to handicap the Slovakian unity. Here, as with the Czechs, the dignity of the folk language was a burning question. A song, "Ho, Slavonians," expresses the proud belief that God has entrusted the Slovakians with their tongue, and asks "Who on earth then shall presume this gift from us to sunder?"

The Czechs and Slovaks have an almost common language, but the dialectal distinctions undoubtedly have been accentuated by the political separation of the two districts over a long period of time. Likewise the folk music, Slavic at base, has undergone distinctive development in each region. As one might expect, the Czech music of Bohemia and Moravia is highly westernized. The old modal scales have given way almost completely to major and minor. The strong sense of form in the songs implies the recent origin of most of the music. The Sudeten German element has been insistent and aggressive in popularizing its own cul-

ture, so that more than twelve thousand German folk songs were discovered in Czech territory during the 1920's, as compared with about fifty thousand in the Czech language. Such a "conscious" minority cannot fail to have affected the growth of folk patterns.

By contrast, Slovakian music is tinged with eastern and southern coloring. Béla Bartók has made a careful study of this region from the viewpoint of a scientific folklorist, and finds the influence of Hungary strong. He differentiates sharply between the ancient and the modern style (paralleled in Hungarian folk music); the ancient style, primitive in scale and structure, is, he says, the clearest example of an indigenous development in Slovakian music. The modern style, a product of the last century, has been formed under the influence of the new style of Hungarian folk music.[1] Most noticeable in our selection of Slovakian songs are, first, the Hungarian style of Czardas syncopation (cf. "We Are Poor," "Seed I Planted," "Fading Youth"), and, secondly, the presence of Oriental colorings in scales, to be attributed to Gypsy rather than to pure Hungarian influence (cf. "Fading Youth" and "Water Running").

In the folk music of both districts one is impressed by the strong rhythms. Here are tunes that can easily be danced to, tunes whose sheer energy provides their own gaiety. The Czechs favor triple time for folk dances such as the Furiant, but there are many Polkas in duple time. The Slovaks, on the other hand, use almost nothing except a two-accent measure. Our songs reflect the characteristic dance rhythms of both groups. Significantly, the further east

---

[1] Béla Bartók, "Les recherches sur le folklore musical en Hongrie," *Art Populaire: Travaux artistiques et scientifiques du Ier Congres International des arts populaires, Prague, 1928* (Paris, 1931), II, 128. Bartók speaks of still a third variety of folk music—a heterogeneous style, indigenous in some respects, but obviously "contaminated" by western influences. Most of the Slovakian songs in our volume are relatively modern and belong to either the "heterogeneous" or the "modern homogeneous" style.

one goes and the further back into the mountains one penetrates, the deeper the melancholy of the reflective song, and the more intense the fiery enthusiasm of dance-tunes.

The half-dozen Bohemian songs in this volume are confined to two topics—love and war. In "The Soldier" the young man is too fascinated by his new trappings to take war very seriously. The white tunic dates this as early nineteenth century. "Yenitchku" is revealing in that between the lines we can read the tragedy of the youth who has been recruited for the army against his will, probably while he was out on a spree. "Are they worth it—your horse and your fine saber?" asks his mother at the close of the song, and the answer is clearly no. These lyrics are so condensed that we have no notion of the historical background; we do not know whether the soldier is part of a mercenary army or of local legions fighting in defense of their own homes. We can conceive the situation only in personal terms, and we are likely to feel that the mother's wistful attitude is entirely proper.

Love is such an important staple of Czechoslovakian lyric that it intrudes in both of the soldier songs. In the other four lyrics it is dominant. "The Promise," scarcely more than a century old, is realistic despite the conventionality of details. It is the familiar story of the maiden whose wedding day is being put off by the evasive young man who is more loved than loving. "Tell Me, Dear" is the conventional compliment to one's beloved, sung to an interesting tune that seems older than others in this group.

"Andulko" and "Swallows Are Flying" are not entirely unrelated in subject. The former is a so-called "night-visit" song in which the lover says that he has stolen to his mistress' house because he can't sleep. The latter, a kind of *aubade*, pictures the lover being sent home at dawn. He is unwilling to go and even provides an excuse for his beloved's not having

done the chores! A. H. Krappe has briefly traced these two international folksong motifs and suggests that they derive from a primitive state of society in which husband and wife lived apart with their respective families. Visits such as those described here were thus normal and conventional. As the social order became more sophisticated, however, says Krappe, the motivation of the songs was altered by later generations of singers to conform to new patterns of courtship.[1]

The Moravian songs continue the motifs of love and war found in the Bohemian selections. Musically they are not of great antiquity, yet the subject-matter suggests a very simple, almost primitive life. A girl would rather throw her lover's ring into the Danube than return it to him; another wishes herself turned into a pigeon, that she might fly to her lover; still another maiden protests against her mother's pessimistic belief, "Once the wedding bell, soon the passing knell." Several of the Bohemian and Moravian songs are dialogues ("The Promise," "Swallows Are Flying," "You Shall Never Have the Ring," "Don't Get Married," "There's No Room for You").

Musically the songs reflect a somber note more intensely than do the words. All but one of them are in minor, and their generally slow tempo distinguishes them from many equally lyrical Slovakian pieces. A typical Moravian rhythmic motif, recurring again and again in these songs, is the Polish mazurka pattern exemplified in "You Shall Never Have the Ring."

Many Moravian districts have absorbed cultural elements from both their eastern and western neighbors. Our "There's No Room for You," taken from a recent Slovakian collection, is such a transitional piece. Its language is Slovakian, but in style its mazurka rhythm is more in accord with native Moravian models. Ostrov (or Ostrau) mentioned in the song is a small town near Brunn, not the larger industrial set-

---

[1] A. H. Krappe, *The Science of Folk-lore* (London, 1930), pp. 158-9.

tlement Morava Ostrava near the northern frontier. Lest the reference to lime tree should seem to imply a geographical inconsistency, it should be pointed out that this is another name for the linden, common throughout temperate latitudes.

The Hungarian influence may be seen in the rhythm and tonality of many Slovakian melodies. "Darling, Come Early" is a czardas tune whose Hungarian flavor lies in the boldly syncopated rhythm. In various forms it has been popular throughout central Europe. In Hungary the melody is in minor, with many Oriental touches; a South Slavic version exists, without the Oriental coloring, but preserving the minor scale. Both variants may be recent "composed" folk-like tunes, but there is no reason to suppose that the Slovakian song is not genuine folk music.

"Coughing" also is a rural love song in dancing rhythm. This is not a narrative piece, but the situation is described clearly enough for us to reconstruct a story. The charming naïveté of this song lies in the absence of any moral censure of the lovers—who, if found, will be compromised.

Warnings against marriage, such as "Wives Aren't Like Maidens," are common in the folksong of almost every nation. A husband may find that his partner is lazy, or a wife may discover that she has married a drunkard. In this mood, the joys of a single life are praised, and the singer momentarily forgets the pangs of love and the sorrows of a loveless life. A current American expression of this theme begins:

> *Single girl, single girl,*
> *She's going dressed fine;*
> *Married girl, a married girl,*
> *She wears just any kind.*

Our Slovakian song, like the Moravian example, "Don't Get Married," is as romantic in spirit as the American song is factual and realistic.

"We Are Poor," "Seed I Planted" and "Fad-

ing Youth" have Hungarian Gypsy rhythmic patterns reminiscent of the "Scotch snap"; they are not in the frenzied tempo of the fast Czardas, but are to be sung *lento* in accordance with their reflective, wistful words. "We Are Poor" is an especially touching song, paradoxical in its imagery. The rosebush is a conventional symbol of romantic love or grief, but the conclusion is pure pathos as we learn that no suitors come to the door because of the family's poverty. Although we associate this sort of sentiment with the melodramas of the '90's, the unrealities of the old gas-light theatre seldom achieve the sincerity of this song.

The tune of "Let Me Keep Faith" has had an unusually active life. It is, first of all, a Slovakian folksong, whose original words constitute a romantic dialogue between a young suitor and a shy maiden. Since the First World War the tune has become the Slovakian National Anthem, sung to words that have been associated with it at least since 1895:

> *Lightens the Tatra,[1] with thunder*
> *the heights are shaken.*
> *Stand fast, my brothers,*
> *Death take the others,*
> *Slovaks shall awaken.*

With typical modifications it occurs among the popular melodies of the Eastern Jews. The tune is sung also in Hungary, and because the Hungarian lyrics seem choicer, they have been chosen to accompany the Slovakian tune.

The remainder of our selections are all love songs. Some are good-humored, but sadness or fatalistic fear of the future predominates. The serenades ("Goodnight," "Evening Star") are similar to our Wendish "Cossack's Farewell." The place-name Nitra (or Neutra) refers to the western Slovakian town from which "Anitchka" was collected; it is also the setting of "Nitra's Bells." "Water Running," an unusual nine-measure melody, is exotic in the Oriental coloring of its scale.

---

[1] A mountain range in northern Slovakia.

255

The Soldier

Called to the ar – my, my girl I must leave. Here is my coat, there's no re – prieve. Fine white coat, can't you see? Fine red stripes, one, two, three, That's what they gave to me!

Called to the army, my girl I must leave.
Give me a horse—I shall not grieve.
Fine black horse, saddle too—
Ah, what deeds I shall do,
Fight like a soldier true!

Vzali mě na vojnu od panny
A bilý kabát mi dali,
Kabátek béloučký,
Červené veyložky,
To mi darovali.

Dostal jsem koníčka vranéko
A pěkně osedlaného,
Tim se těsit budu,
Až odtud pojedu
Do pole širého.

Andulko

An – dul – ko, my dar – ling, An – dul – ko, my dar – ling, Though I've tried, sleep

would not come. Now I've come to see you, now I've come to see you.

Far from you, all's wear – i – some.

Late I traveled homeward, late I traveled homeward.
Master scolds, "Why come so late?"
"Please forgive me, Master, please forgive me, Master,
Not my fault, *she* made me late."

Anduličko moje, nedala's pokoje,
Nedala's mi v noci spát,
Nedala's mi spáti, já, jsem musil vstáti,
Musil jsem tě milovat.

Já jsem domů přišel, když měsíček vyšel,
Sedlák měl nakrmeno:
Můj sedláče zlatý, já jsem byl zajatý
U děvčete švarného.

Yenitchku

Ye - nitch-ku, poor fel - low, had you then heard Moth-er,

Now you'd wear no sab - er, wear no coat red - bord -ered,

Now you'd wear no sab - er, ride no horse black – coat - ed,

Nor would you, son, have to car - ry out harsh ord -ers.

260

Yenitchku, poor fellow, had you then heard Mother,
Still you might live here and court your sweet Anitchka.
Someone else now courts her, someone will soon win her.
Son, are they worth it—your horse and your fine saber?

Kdybys byl, Jeníčku, poslouchal matičku,
Nebyl bys ted nosil po straně šavličku.
Neměl bys šavličku a koně vraného:
Nebyl bys poslouchal člověka cizího.

The Promise

"A – dam – ku dear, what do you fear?

Keep now the pro – mise, boy, Which once you made with joy.

Why must I pine? Say you'll be mine!

"Andulko dear, wait till next year.
Wait till the spring arrives,
Wait till my planting thrives.
Then you'll not pine, then you'll be mine.
Wait till the spring arrives,
Wait till my planting thrives.
Then you'll not pine, then you'll be mine.

"Andulko dear, be of good cheer!
Till death lays hands on me,
You will my sweetheart be,
None else beside! You'll be my bride!
Till death lays hands on me,
You will my sweetheart be,
None else beside! You'll be my bride!

Adámku náš! Co pak děláš?
Na louce ti pasou,
Ty jsi mezi chasou,
Ty nic nedbáš, ty nic nedbáš.
Na louce ti pasou,
Ty jsi mezi chasou,
Ty nic nedbáš, ty nic nedbáš!

Adámku můj! Vslovu mně stůj.
Co jsi mně sliboval,
Když jsi mne miloval,
Že budeš můj, že budeš můj.
Co jsi mně sliboval,
Když jsi mne miloval,
Ze budeš můj, že budeš můj.

Andulko má! Není možná:
Počkej jen do jara,
Až bude fiala,
Pak budeš má, pak budeš má.
Počkej jen do jara,
Až bude fiala,
Pak budeš má, pak budeš má.

Andulko má roztomilá!
Do smrti nejdelší
Moje nejmilejší
Zádná jiná, žádná jiná.
Do smrti nejdelší
Moje nejmilejší
Žádná jiná, žádná jiná!

Swallows Are Flying

"Mother would beat me, beat me, dear,
When she found out, alas!
Mother would beat me, beat me, dear,
When she found out, alas!
Why I'd not fed the cows,
Not even mowed the grass,
Not fed the cows their grass today,
Not fed the cows their grass."

"No, she won't beat you, beat you, dear.
Didn't it rain last night?
No, she won't beat you, beat you, dear.
Didn't it rain last night?
Wet grass you cannot mow.
Then, dear, I need not go.
So we will be all right, my dear,
So we will be all right."

Vlaštovička lítá, lítá, povídá, že svítá,
Vlaštovička lítá, lítá, povídá, že svítá:
Jdi, Jeníčku, domů,
Pomoci ti nemohu,
Já bych byla bita, bita,
Já bych byla bita.

Já bych byla bita, bita od svojí matičky,
Já bych byla bita, bita od svojí matičky:
Že jsem nenažala,
Kravičkám nedala
Zelené travičky, vičky,
Zelené travičky.

Ty bita nebudeš, 'budeš, na trávu nepůjdeš,
Ty bita nebudeš, 'budeš, na trávu nepůjdeš:
Napadla rosička,
Studená vodička,
Není to lež žádná, žádná,
Není to lež žádná.

Tell Me, Dear

Tell me, dear—dear, tell me
Why your eyes so move me.
Seeing them one moment,
All my world goes whirling,
Whirling so fast for me.

Tell me, dear—dear, tell me
Why your face so moves me.
When my eyes can't see it,
All my heart starts aching,
Aching so hard in me.

Co to máš, má milá,
Co to máš, za čelo:
Jak jsem tě políbil,
Celé se zardělo,
Celé se zardělo.

Co to máš, má milá,
Co to máš za oči:
Když do nich pohlédnu,
Svět se se mnou točí,
Svět se se mnou točí.

Co to máš, má milá,
Co to máš za líce,
Když já jich nevidim,
Bolívá mě srdce,
Bolívá mě srdce.

Where the Grass Is Growing

I must leave my sweetheart now for ever.
Parting—that's a sickness worse than fever.
Only find the healing herb, fever soon is ended.
Broken hearts are never, never mended.

Jenom ty mně, má panenko, pověz,
Kam ty ráno na travěnku půjdeš?
A já půjdu, půjdu, půjdu do hájíčka,
Zelená se tam pěkná travička.

Zelenej se, travěnko zelená,
Rozlívej se, voděnko studená;
Rozlívej se, rozlívej po hladkém kamení,
Nastalo mně milým rozlúčení.

Rozlúčení, co je to těžká věc,
To je horší nežli jaká bolest!
Od bolesti zelená, zelená bylinka,
Od tesknosti je hezká panenka.

There's No Room for You

How she list-ens, to her sol-dier cling-ing!

"Farewell, darling! God preserve and guide you!
All this long year, I'll not be beside you."
"If this long year you may not come home, dear,
Take me with you—gladly I will come, dear."

"Darling, darling, think of what you're saying!
I must go now. Hear my sorrel neighing!
If I tried to take you on his back, dear,
Where, then, tell me, would I put my pack, dear?"

"Come, dear, look, dear! There his grain I steady,
Here on this side, hangs my saber ready,
There on that side, gun and pistol too, dear.
So you see, dear, there's no room for you, dear!"

Od Ostrova usekaná cesta
Chodí po nej frajeročka herská,
Chodí, chodí ruky zalamuje,
Že jej milý, do vojny rukuje.

Milá, milá, s Bohom si tu zostaň,
Už neprídem toho roku nazpät.
Keď neprídeš toho roku nazpät,
Mohol bysi aj mňa zo sebou vziať.

Milá, milá, či bys to žiadala,
Aby ťa vzal na vraného koňa,
Dobre vidíš, že tesno sedieť mám,
Kolo seba spakovaný sersám.

Na predku mám futráš pre koníčka,
Ja na lavom mi visí šablička,
Ja na pravom, tam mi visí pištoľ,
Môžeš vedieť, že nemôžem byť tvoj.

Don't Get Married

"What is that you're saying?
Young girls can't get married!
Take me to the graveyard,
Show me where they're buried
Girls who married all too young,
Girls whose passing-bells have rung!"

Ma miła ceruško,
Něvdavaj se ešče,
Ludě povědaju,
Že si młade děvče.
Že ty młade ženky mřu,
Co se skoro vdavaju.

Ma miła mamulko,
Přes krchov choditě,
Kdě vy tam ty hroby
Mładych žen poznatě.
Že ty młade ženky mřu,
Co se skoro vdavaju.

You Shall Never Have the Ring

"Give it back, dear, give it back, dear! What I gave you, give it back, dear!

Ring of gold and pre-cious stone Giv-en when you were my own.

"Give it back, dear, give it back, dear!
Ring I gave you, give it back, dear!
Change of time brings change of heart,
Change of time says we must part."

"No, I will not, will not give it.
Never, never will I give it.
Sooner will I let it fall,
Break to pieces, stone and all.

"Sooner will I, cruel giver,
Take it, throw it in the river.
You shall never have my ring,
You shall never have my ring!"

Vrat' mi, milá, vrat' mi ten dar,
Co jsem ti na památku dal,
Vrat' mi, milá, prstýnek,
Je vněm zlatý kamínek.

Než bych ti ho, synku, dala.
Radši bych ho roztrískala,
Hodila do Dunaje,
Tam ho žádný nenajde.

Would I Were a Pigeon

Perched before his window, singing beneath the blue sky,
Oh, how sad I'd make him! Then, how my sweetheart would cry!

Would I were a pigeon! Over the mountain I'd wing,
Find my sweetheart's window. Then, oh, how sweetly I'd sing!

Ach, dybych já byla tú bílú holubičkú,
Já bych sa nadnésla svém milém nad svétničku.

A já bych si sedla, oj, najeho okénko,
Až' by zaplakalo, oj, vném jeho srdénko.

Darling, Come Early

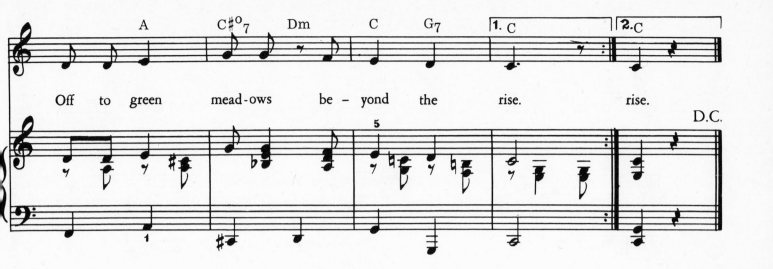

Off to green mead-ows be – yond the rise.　rise.

D.C.

Come, and you'll see, dear, my love so strong.
When I have finished, I sing a song.
Work, dear, or play, dear, this I dare say, dear:
All the day, darling, for you I long.
Work, dear, or play, dear, this I dare say, dear:
All the day, darling, for you I long.

Prídi ty, šuhajko, ráno k nám,
Uvidíš, čo ja to robievam,
Ja ráno vstávam, kravy napájam,
Ovečky na pole vyháňam.
Ja ráno vstávam, kravy napájam,
Ovečky na pole vyháňam.

A keď si tú prácu vykonam,
Potom si veselo zaspievam,
A pri tom speve, ako pri práci,
Zavše len na teba myslievam.
A pri tom speve, ako pri práci,
Zavše len na teba myslievam.

Coughing

Hat and coat they would take, take from me.

Sunday hat they would take, feathered fine,
Sunday coat, trimmed with braid, sweetheart mine.
What is that, Anitchka? Coughing, dear?
Silent be! No one else knows you're here!
What is that, Anitchka? Coughing, dear?
Silent be! No one else knows you're here!

Anička, dušička, nekašli,
Aby ma pri tebe nenašli;
Bo ak ma pri tebe očujú,
Vesmú mi klobúčik i šubu.
Bo ak ma pri tebe očujú,
Vesmú mi klobúčik i šubu.

Vezmú mi klobúčik s perami
I šubu vlnenú s šnúrami.
Anička, dušička, nekašli,
Aby ma pri tebe nenašli.
Anička, dušička, nekašli,
Aby ma pri tebe nenašli.

Go Away, You Wicked Fellows!

Go a - way, you wick - ed fell - ows, I can't bear you!

Give a dance and not in - vite me! Do I scare you?

All night long I would have stayed there, Giv - en gold to those who played there.

I'd have e - ven kissed you good - night! night!

Mother tried her best to please you, took such trouble!
How she's made the oven roar, the kettle bubble!
All the cookies she's been making,
All the cakes that she's been baking—
All done so I'd get to your dance!
All the cookies she's been making,
All the cakes that she's been baking—
All done so I'd get to your dance!

Well, it's too late *this* time, now the party's ended.
Also, I have heard, "least said is soonest mended."
Really, I can't go on hating.
Ask me next time. I'll be waiting.
Even though it's midnight, I'll come!
Really, I can't go on hating.
Ask me next time. I'll be waiting.
Even though it's midnight, I'll come!

Bodaj by vás, vy mládenci čerti vzali,
Ked' ste vy mňa na ten tanec nepozvali
Ja by bola tancovala
Aj na cimbal niečo dala
Aj vás všetkych pobozkala.
Ja by bola tancovala
Aj na cimbal niečo dala
Aj vás všetkých pobozkala.

Čo sa mamka tejto noci natrápila,
Aby sa vám len nejako zavd'ačila
Spiekla múky za tri korce
Pre vás chlapci na koláče,
Len aby som tancovala.
Spiekla múky za tri korce
Pre vás chlapci na koláče,
Len aby som tancovala.

Už je ameň, už je koniec, milí chlapci,
Ked' je už raz, ked' je už raz po tom tanci,
Ked' sa nový tanec strhne,
Pamätajte chlapci na mne,
Trebars bude po pol noci.
Ked' sa nový tanec strhne,
Pamätajte chlapci na mne,
Trebars bude po pol noci.

Wives Aren't Like Maidens

Wives live in pri - son, but girls un - wed are fre - er than fish.

Maidens go walking and merry are they,
Smiling and flirting and singing all day.
Maidens pick flowers, gay garlands they make.
Garlands well-woven a maiden twines for true-love's dear sake.

Twining her garland, a maiden sings low.
Off to her sweetheart next morning she'll go,
Bring him her garland—how happy they'll be!
Daughter, don't marry! A girl who marries young, dear—sad she!

Nevydávaj sa ty dievča ešte,
Lepšie je dievčatu, jak neveste;
Dievčatko si chodí po slobode
Ako tá rybôčka v bystrej vode, v bystrej vode.

Keď ide po poli, veselí sa,
Keď vidí šuhajka, zasmeje sa;
Nasbiera si kviet'a všeljakého,
Uvije perečko pre milého, pre milého.

Keď skladá a vije to perečko,
Horí od ľúbosti jej srdiečko;
Za rána bárskedy pierko oddá:
Mladého dievčat'a vydat' škoda, vydat' škoda.

We Are Poor

"Stands a rosebush bearing flowers by our cottage door.
Tell me, daughter, does no suitor come here any more?"
"No one ever comes here, Mother,
Neither he nor any other.
All the village fears us, Mother, Mother, we are poor."

Pod tým naším okinečkom býva veľký mráz
A v tej našej studenečke nieto vody zas;
Vezmem si ja sekerečku,
Prerúbem tu studenečku,
A v tej našej studenečke bude voda zas.

Pod tým naším okinečkom z bielej ruže kvet,
Povedz že mi, moja milá, čo ťa mrzí svet?
A mňa svet ten nič nemrzí,
A mňa svet ten nič nemrzí,
Len mňa moje srdce bolí, plakala by hned.

Pod tým naším okinečkom biela lálija,
Povedz že mi, moja milá, kto k vám chodieva?
A k nám nikto nechodieva,
A k nám nikto nechodieva,
Lebo sa mňa každý bojí, že som chudobná.

Let Me Keep Faith

Peo - ple say. "Don't take him, bet - ter choose the oth - er!"

Peo - ple say, "Don't take him, bet - ter choose the oth - er!"

Peo - ple say, "Choose wise - ly Think of six

fine ox - en!" But how can I, Moth - er?

When my love looks at me, I forget the other.
When my love looks at me, I forget the other.
What are then six oxen?
Not for nine kings' ransoms
Would I leave him, Mother!
What are then six oxen?
Not for nine kings' ransoms
Would I leave him, Mother!

Mother dear, don't tell me I should wed the other.
Mother dear, don't tell me I should wed the other.
Do not say *that*, Mother.
Let me keep faith, Mother.
I have promised, Mother!
Do not say *that*, Mother.
Let me keep faith, Mother.
I have promised, Mother!

U studienky stála, napájala páva,
U studienky stála, napájala páva,
Kebych ja vedela,
Čieho budem pána,
Čieho budem pána.
Kebych ja vedela,
Čieho budem pána,
Čieho budem pána.

Kebych ja vedela, kde ja budem bývat',
Kebych ja vedela, kde ja budem bývat',
Chodievala by som,
Lavičky mnývat',
Lavičky mnývat'.
Chodievala by som,
Lavičky mnývat',
Lavičky mnývat'.

Umývala bych jich hrachovým vechtíkom,
Umývala bych jich hrachovým vechtíkom,
Utierala bych jich,
Hodbabným ručníkom,
Hodbabným ručníkom.
Utierala bych jich,
Hodbabným ručníkom,
Hodbabným ručníkom.

Kebych ja vedela, kde ja budem bývat',
Kebych ja vedela, kde ja budem bývat',
Veru by som išla,
Ližičky mnývat',
Ližičky mnývat'.
Veru by som išla,
Ližičky mnývat',
Ližičky mnývat'.

A nie len ližičky, ale i mistički,
A nie len ližičky, ale i mistički,
Žeby bolo pekne,
U mojej mamičky,
U mojej mamičky.
Žeby bolo pekne,
U mojej mamičky,
U mojej mamičky.

Seed I Planted

Seed I plant-ed, not a flow-er bloomed this year.

So my sweet-heart, when I call her, will not hear.

Flow-ers fail me, sweet-heart fails me, so things go.

What a sor-ry place the world is, well I know.

Zasadil som fialenku, nezišla,
Zavolal som na milenku, nevyšla,
Sklamala ma moja milá, tiež aj kvet,
Nepreje mi ničt dobrého celý svet.
Sklamala ma moja milá, tiež aj kvet,
Nepraje mi ničt dobrého celý svet.

Láska je len preveliké súžení,
Na ném srdci ťažký kámeň vložený;
Ale dá Boh ešte dožiť taký čas,
Že ma milá ráda výnde na môj hlas.
Ale dá Boh ešte dožiť taký čas,
Že ma milá ráda výnde na môj hlas.

Fading Youth

Faded youth is soon discarded,
Lies forgotten, unregarded.
All at last forsake it—woe's me—
Father, mother, lover, all three!

Youth and beauty from me going,
Like the stream so swiftly flowing!
Streams renew their waters, flow on.
No return for beauty, once gone.

Veje vetor po doline,
Moja mladosť len tak hynie,
Len tak hynie, aj zahynie,
Ako lístok v bukovine.

Keď uvadne dolu spadne,
Nikto sa naň neohliadne,
Ani otec, ani matka,
Ani žiadna kamarátka.

Moja mladosť i podoba
Tak mi hynie ako voda:
Voda zhynie, druhá príde,
Moja mladosť už nepríde.

The Slovak

"Mountains so high, mountains so dear, tell me true,
Will it be long ere I your woods wander through?
Will there be buds, will there be snow falling chill?
When I come home will my sweet bride love me still?"

Keď sa Slovák preč do světa ubieral,
Pri vesnici na kopečku zavolal,
Zavolal on na kopečku po dvakrát:
S Bohom otec, s Bohom máci, sestra, brat!

Povedz mně ty, mój kopečku vysoký,
Či t'a uzrím za dva lebo tri roky,
Či já budzem ešče vidzec moju mác,
Či mňa budze moja milá milovac?

Pretty Miller's Daughter

geese to wa-ter, Wish I had not!"

D.C.

"Right by the bank I stumbled,
Splash, in the water tumbled—
Wet all over!
Right by the bank I stumbled,
Splash, in the water tumbled—
Wet all over!
As I scrambled out, all dripping,
Passed my lover.
As I scrambled out, all dripping,
Passed my lover."

Anička mlynárova,
Mášli ty húsky doma,
Mášli, mášli?
Anička mlynárova,
Mášli ty húsky doma,
Mášli, mášli?
Ved' ti ony za vodičku,
Zašly, zašly.
Ved' ti ony za vodičku,
Zašly, zašly.

Zašly ti za vodienku
Zmáčal som košelienku,
Zmáčal, zmáčal.
Zašly ti za vodienku
Zmáčal som košelienku,
Zmáčal, zmáčal.
Ked' som si ja k mojej milej,
Kráčal, kráčal.
Ked' som si ja k mojej milej,
Kráčal, kráčal.

295

Anitchka

"An - itch - ka, tell me, my pret - ty, sweet pet,

Where did you get both your slip - pers so wet?"

"There in the oak for - est, Where we cut grass, dear - est.

That   is   where   I   wet   them,   my   pet.   pet."

"Three days I mowed there, my pretty sweet pet,
Three days I mowed, but my slippers weren't wet.
When I was done mowing,
Back to your house going,
Through the brook I waded, my pet.
When I was done mowing,
Back to your house going,
Through the brook I waded, my pet."

Anička, dušička, kde si bola,
Keď' si si čižmičky zarosila?
Bola som v hájičku,
Žala som trávičku,
Duša moja, duša moja.
Bola som v hájičku,
Žala som trávičku,
Duša moja, duša moja.

A ja som po tri dni trávu kosil,
Ešte som si čižmy nezarosil.
A ja som hrabala,
Teba som čakala,
Duša moja, duša moja.
A ja som hrabala,
Teba som čakala,
Duša moja, duša moja.

Goodnight

Darling, my darling, goodnight, goodnight,
God keep you safely till morning-light!
May your sleep peaceful be,
All through the night, may you dream of me!
May your sleep peaceful be,
All through the night, may you dream of me!

Dobrú noc, má milá, dobrú noc!
Nech ti je sám Pán Boh na pomoc!
Dobrú noc, dobre spi:
Nech sa ti snívajú sladké sny.
Dobrú noc, dobre spi:
Nech sa ti snívajú sladké sny.

Snívaj sa ti sníček, len snívaj,
Keď vstaneš sníčeku vieru daj,
Že ťa ja milujem,
Srdiečko svoje ti darujem.
Že ťa ja milujem,
Srdiečko svoje ti darujem.

Could You Not Come

When darkness fell, my dear,
Oh, how I shook with fear!
Trembled when moonlight shone,
Sitting here all alone,
Still all alone, dear.
Trembled when moonlight shone,
Sitting here all alone,
Still all alone, dear.

Let me no longer fear!
This is my life, my dear:
Wretched, when you're away,
Happy but when you say,
"Sweetheart, I love you."
Wretched, when you're away,
Happy but when you say,
"Sweetheart, I love you."

Proč si k nám nepryšeu?
Já som tě čekala!
Na lávě seděla,
Z okénka hleděla,
Dušenko moja!
Na lávě seděla,
Z okénka hlědela,
Dušenko moja!

Teskno ma svíralo,
Ked' sa už ztmívalo,
Měsíc ten už vyšeu,
Milý moj neprišeu
K milence svojej.
Měsíc ten už vyšeu,
Milý moj neprišeu
K milence svojej.

Ach! jak už okrývám,
Ked' na tě pozírám,
Se mnú ked' hovorýš
A vrúcně proslovíš:
Milenko moja!
Se mnú ked' hovorýš
A vrúcně proslovíš:
Milenko moja!

Evening Star

night, sleep you, Safe - ly sleep, An - itch - ka.

Now goodnight, goodnight now!
Not to all say I so.
Only my own sweeting
Greet I with this greeting,
Only my own sweeting,
Her from whom now I go.

Vysoko zornička,
Dobrú noc Anička;
Eš te vyššie nebe,
Pán Bôh daj aj tebe.
Eš te vyššie nebe,
Pán Bôh daj aj tebe.

Dobrú noc, dobrú noc,
Ale nie každému,
Len tomu dievčátku,
Čo ja chodím k nemu.
Len tomu dievčátku,
Čo ja chodím k nemu.

Early, My Dear

Such a real-ly pret-ty sweet-heart, face with-out flaw,

On-ly ve-ry skil-ful paint-ers ev-er could draw.

Oh, what white cheeks! Oh, what black eyes!

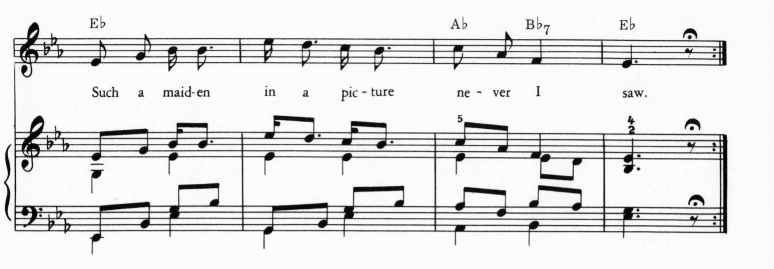

Such a maid-en   in a pic-ture   ne-ver I   saw.

Now I suffer bitter sorrow, suffer deep woe,
For tomorrow morning, darling, hence I must go.
Early, my dear, early, my dear,
When the earliest morning sunbeam lights the high snow.

Takú som si frajerôčku zamiloval,
Ako by ju malireček vymaľoval:
Oči čierne, biele líčka,
Jako by ju maľovala malirečka.

Ale už je, moja mila, všetko darmo,
Už ja musím mašírovat saj'tra ráno;
Saj'tra ráno, skoro ráno,
Skur než vynde jasné slnko nad Komárno.

Nitra's Bells

wed – ded all my life.

Always I will pray for him, who was my love so long.
Never would I wish him ill, nor ever do him wrong.
May the Lord my sweetheart bless, bless my sweetheart's wife!
Bless not me—I shall remain unwedded all my life.

Tie Nitrinske hodiny veľ'mi zle bijú,
Už si môj milý vedie k oltáru inú.
Nech mu Pán Boh pomáhá v jeho manželství,
A ja budem strvávať' ve svém panenství.

Zle bych mu vinšuvala, to mu nebudem,
Že bych ho preklnala to tiež nebudem.
Nech mu Pán Boh pomáha v jeho manželství,
A ja budem strvávať' ve svém panenství.

The Czardas

When I first was draft – ed, on - ly last fall,

Then I did not care for mus - ic at all.

Now to war we're go – ing, now the wine is flow – ing,

Now, mu - si - cians, for a čar - daš I call!

Now the band has started. Listen, they play!
Now my tears are flowing, weeping this day.
Were you here, my beauty, I'd forget my duty,
On my horse I'd set you, take you away!

Ked' som na tu vojnu narukoval,
Ani som si čardáš zahrát nedal.
Kamarádi moji, jedeme do vojny,
Zahrajte mi čardáš po mej vůli.

Muzika ne počala čardáš hrát,
Počaly ně zoček slzy kapat.
Frajerenko moja, kebys tady bola,
Posadil bych t'a na mého koňa.

Water Running

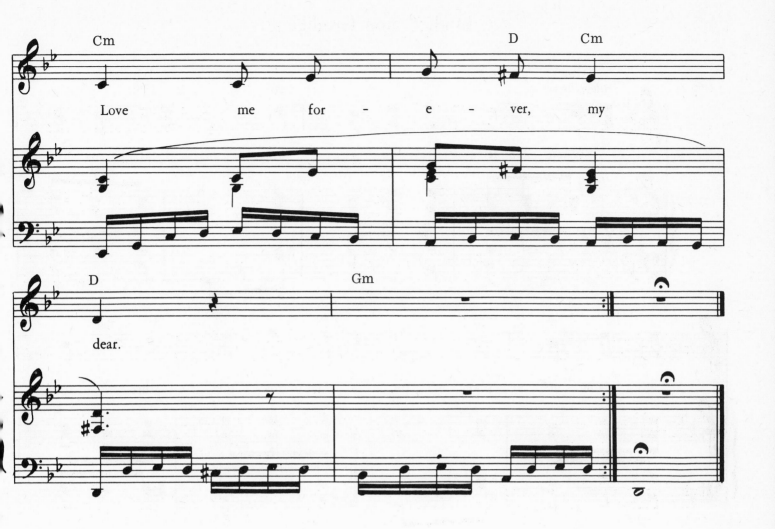

Water running ever,
Rustling through grass and pebbles!
He who suffered never,
Much he will suffer from love.

Water running—hear it—
Sings softly round my cottage.
Darling, do not fear it,
I have not spoken your name.

Valley deeply hidden,
Valley so dear, my valley!
Love is not forbidden.
No one shall know that we love.

Tečie voda, tečie,
Ej, do potôčka kvapká:
Miluj že ma miluj,
Ej, moja duša sladká.

Tečie voda, tečie,
Ej, po kameňoch huči
Kto vzdychat' neumie,
Ej, láska ho naučí.

Tečie, voda, tečie,
Ej, kolo nášho domu,
Koho ja milujem,
Ej, nepoviem nikomu.

Dolina, dolina,
Ej, medzi dolinami,
Žiaden človek nevie,
Ej, čo je medzi nami.

Mother, Stop Grumbling!

"Mother, stop grumbling and scolding.
Put down the switch you are holding.
Someone who comes to see me
Now wears a saber to free me!"

"If you keep grumbling, or harm me,
I shall enlist in the army.
Better not drive me to it!
Scold me once more, and I'll do it!"

A na tom zvolenskom moste
Hraly sa dievčence v kocke;
Hraly sa ony, hraly, doma ich mamičky lály.
Hraly sa ony, hraly, doma ich mamičky lály.

Nelaj ma, mat' moja, nelaj,
Pride mi na večer šuhaj;
Na peknom bielom koni, šabľa mu pri boku zvoní.
Na peknom bielom koni, šabľa mu pri boku zvoní.

Ak ma vy budete láti,
Dám sa vám ja zverbovati;
Sadnem si ja na koňa, pôjdem ta, kde bude vojna!
Sadnem si ja na koňa, pôjdem ta, kde bude vojna!

Hungarian

THE DISMEMBERMENT of the Austro-Hungarian Empire after the First World War was not the destructive act it may at first glance seem to be. For actually the old Dual Monarchy was united only in the person of the Emperor. The sprawling territory at the crossroads of central Europe was ethnically very miscellaneous, and one of the notable sources of its difficulty during the last half century of its existence was the struggle of each linguistic and racial group for autonomy. The Treaty of Versailles, for all its resultant compromises and inequalities, attempted to fix new boundary lines in accordance with a spirit of self-determination of peoples. Thus was formed the kingdom of the Serbs, Croats and Slovenes (known as Yugoslavia); thus the new state for the Czechs and the Slovaks. The new Austria comprised the German-speaking areas of the old Empire, the new Hungary most of the Magyar regions.

The terms Hungary and Hungarian have thus been more nearly synonymous since 1920 than at any time in the past. Once the Rumanian and South Slavic regions had been cut away, the Hungary that remained was ninety percent Magyar, a fact of especial importance in any discussion of Hungarian social history. For this once Asiatic people which settled the mid-Danubian regions a thousand years ago has preserved a remarkable homogeneity. Their language is unrelated to any of the Indo-European tongues, and Hungarian influence on the outside world was never great enough to popularize the language as a cultural or political instrument. Hungarians often had to learn another language for communication purposes, but few foreigners ever bothered to learn the difficult Magyar. As a result, the language gave the people an identity, and probably was as effective as racial and physical boundaries in preventing their scattering and disintegration.

For most of what we know today about Hungarian folk music we are indebted to Béla Bartók, the scholarly composer and musicologist who achieved a tremendous pioneering work in scientifically recording and studying thousands of folk songs. Bartók and his associate Zoltán Kodály found the richest treasures in Transylvania, which, though predominantly Rumanian, has a western fringe and several interior islands of Hungarian population. Here, especially in the southeastern regions of the Szeklers, are to be found remnants of an ancient style of folk music, with primitive pentatonic scales (such as one finds by playing the black keys on the piano). In this old style there is much individual ornamentation at the performer's will, and a free rhythm which Bartók called "recitativo-parlando"—"singing in recitative, whereby the rhythm of the text at times changes the form of the melody in every verse." [1] This ancient style has been rapidly disappearing and can be found only among elderly people in isolated Hungarian communities. In its place has developed a very different folk idiom. The new manner, which has been evolving for over a century, is more architectonic—it has obviously been influenced by the art song of the West—and less variable in rhythm. The fact that the new songs are used for dancing is in part responsible for the popularity of tunes in strict time.

The peculiarities of the Hungarian language have affected the rhythm of even the most recent native folk music. Since all words are accented on the first syllable, songs almost never begin with a "pick-up," or *Auftakt,* which is so frequently found in songs of Western Europe. Hungarian pronunciation probably accounts for some of the marked rhythmic syncopations, including the so-called "Scotch snap"

for an example, see "The Hussar," measure 3).

Most conspicuous in Hungarian popular music is, of course, the Gypsy influence. Brahms and Liszt popularized Hungarian melodies which passed for folk tunes, and since they had been played by Gypsies it was assumed that Gypsy and Hungarian folk music were one and the same. Now we know otherwise. The most popular orchestras in Hungarian towns and cities were manned by Gypsies, whose primary role was one of interpretation, and whose music reflected the taste of their audiences. Almost none of their music was genuine folk art, but consisted rather of "composed" tunes with folk coloring, the work usually of accomplished amateur musicians. All but four or five of the themes of Liszt's Hungarian Rhapsodies and Brahms' Hungarian Dances are of this sort, and the names of many of the composers are actually known. Thus—and this is an important point—much of what passes today as genuine Magyar folk music is not; it is Hungarian art-music of a rather skillful imitative sort, played by Gypsy musicians. The Gypsies tend to make any music their own through their excessive ornamentation, especially in the brilliant violin and cembalo parts, and by their exaggerated tempos and over-obvious sentimentality. Whether it is a lyric with dragging slurs, in which the Gypsy "makes his violin cry," or a Czardas song in dizzying dance tempo, the Gypsy musician extracts the maximum of emotion, and his mannerisms are always conspicuous. The frequent use of a scale with Oriental coloring distinguishes their café music from genuine folksong. "That's My Girl" and "Love's My Permit" among our selections are thus suspect, because they use the augmented second interval which, according to Bartók, does not exist in Hungarian folk music.

To this generalization about Gypsy music one important exception should be made. \The Gypsies of the agricultural villages differ

---

[1] Béla Bartók and Zoltán Kodály, *Folksongs* [of the Transylvanian Hungarians] (Budapest, 1921), p. 5.

greatly from their city brothers; they work on their farms and almost never travel far from their homes. Their music, of a far more primitive sort, is derived almost completely from the Hungarian peasants with whom they associate constantly. Liszt and other nineteenth-century musicians thought they had captured the genuine spirit of the Hungarian folk; but they traveled hastily through the country listening briefly to orchestras which played the most pretentious and up-to-date things they knew. One cannot plumb the depths of a folk tradition from an observation platform, as Liszt's elaborately wrongheaded book on *The Gipsy in Music* (1859) proves.

Almost all the Hungarian songs in this collection are strongly Gypsy, or are peasant songs influenced by Gypsy rhythm or harmony. From "Latzika and Marishka" to "Love's My Permit" the first ten are rather recent creations which are not strictly folk music; but neither composer nor poet is associated with the songs. They are sung all over Hungary and have been included in twentieth-century collections. Most of them are typical Czardas tunes with light-hearted words. Several of them ("That's My Girl," "I've a Purse," "The Hussar") have only a single stanza in the original: Mr. Trask has in each case (as also in "Cherry Gathering," "The Draftee," "Forget the World," "Woe, Woe, Mother Mine") added a second stanza for the purposes of vocal performers. Quite clearly these dancing tunes were popular for their lively rhythm, the lushness of their minor tonality, and their simple architecture. All of this group through "The Hussar" are commonplace love lyrics, simple but not primitive. Several of them are dialogues. The obviousness of the imagery drawn from nature, plus the saccharine clichés of love, makes the words embarrassingly slight in contrast to the music. "Love's My Permit" seems more realistic. A young girl, about to lose her soldier lover, asks the captain to allow her to follow the troops as a sutler (a dealer in military supplies).

If this volume were intended as a representative survey of each nation's folksongs, we should include a large class of songs omitted by design. Many of Béla Bartók's collected items are exotic peasant songs, brief, sometimes without definite form or tonality—especially the "parlando-rubato" songs of which we have already spoken. They prove conclusively that Hungarian folk music is an independent genre, not necessarily connected with the Gypsy at all—music with an individuality no more to be duplicated in Europe than is the Hungarian language. They are treasures for the scientific folklorist, and may become invaluable thematic material for imaginative formal composers; but they would be only *curiosa* for the general public.

We have, however, included some very interesting examples from the collections of Bartók and Kodály, peasant songs and dances rather more familiar in style than some of the chants. "Cherry Gathering," which Bartók says is "probably derived from an art song," comes from Maros-Torda, a Hungarian district in Transylvania. In the romantic treatment of the subject-matter, the cherry harvest becomes not the occasion of a work song, but the vehicle for light amatory sentiment.

"The Draftee," like "The Hussar," reminds us that in olden times October 1 was the day on which young men of twenty-one were called up to begin their peace-time military service. To some Hungarians that old custom must seem nostalgic in these days when they find themselves in the shadow of a great neighboring power.

"Gypsy Tinker," also a Transylvanian song, is interesting as it affords us a picture of the itinerant Gypsy workman. In him there is none of the glamor that usually surrounded the Gypsy musicians who led a public international life amid acclaim. This song reminds us of the repressive laws passed all over Europe against Gypsies. In every country they were subject to constant arrest as vagrants if they stayed overnight in any locality. The result was that the nomadic Gypsies had their careers determined for them: they had to keep moving from place to place, doing whatever odd jobs they could find on the way. The narrator in this song recounts how he once was a respectable peddler with useful merchandise—brooms, thread, kitchen utensils. Now he cannot get even the meanest kind of repair work. The Gypsy bands were victims of all kinds of popular superstitions. They were accused of child-stealing, of having supernatural powers, of spreading malignant disease; but their plight was as much the *result* as the cause of their cruel treatment.

"Forget the World" and "Woe, Woe, Mother Mine" are from districts southwest of Budapest. The former is a drinking song with romantic grief the theme; the latter is a girl's complaint that her Hussar has her kerchief with her name on it, and she is anxious lest he discard it (and her) and so subject her to public scorn and pity.

"Szilvás Village" is a pathetic song of a young shepherd who cannot resist going to a tavern when he knows there is likely to be a fray. He wishes to see blood flow, but when the song ends it is his own body that is being escorted to the tomb, his own mother who is being comforted. Bartók has noted that the music of this song betrays western Slavic influences, that the "shrunken" inner phrases of fewer than four measures are to be paralleled in Moravia and Slovakia.

Pleased to Meet You!

"So much pride in one young fellow isn't right!
Does he think a girl will love him right on sight?
Hope he won't come to call
He's not my type at all,
Pleased to meet you! Now, goodnight!
Hope he won't come to call
He's not my type at all,
Pleased to meet you! Now, goodnight!"

"Stop, my pretty little pigeon, dear as life!
Tell me, don't you really want to be my wife?"
Let us just leave it there.
Men deceive everywhere.
Pleased to meet you! Now, goodnight!
"Let us just leave it there.
Men deceive everywhere.
Pleased to meet you! Now, goodnight!

"Well, I think perhaps I'd like to be your wife,
If you'll promise you'll reform your wicked life.
I don't care—no, not I!
If you don't want to try,
Pleased to meet you! Now, goodnight!
"I don't care—no, not I!
If you don't want to try,
Pleased to meet you! Now, goodnight!"

"Four and four makes eight and nine makes seventeen.
You'll get old and gray, and I won't give a bean."
That is not your affair,
Run along—I won't care!
Pleased to meet you! Now, goodnight!
That is not your affair,
Run along—I won't care!
Pleased to meet you! Now, goodnight!"

"Six and six makes twelve, and nine makes twenty-one.
I would like a kiss from you, my pretty one!"
"No you don't—not today!
Wait your turn. Now I say,
Pleased to meet you! Now, goodnight!
No you don't—not today!
Wait your turn. Now I say,
Pleased to meet you! Now, goodnight!"

Ez a kis lány jaj be rangos egy jószág,
Talán azért huzza össze az orrát,
Mi köze hozzája,
Menjen a dolgára,
Alázatos szolgája.
Mi köze hozzája,
Menjen a dolgára,
Alázatos szolgája.

Ez a legény jaj be rangos egy ficsúr,
Tán azt hiszi mindenkinek szemet szúr!
Mi köze hozzája,
Nam vagyok utjába,
Alázatos szolgája.
Mi köze hozzája,
Nam vagyok utjába,
Alázatos szolgája.

Ugyan édes kis galambom violám!
Lennél-e a feleségem igazán?
Mi köze hozzája,
Hamis a zuzája,
Alázatos szolgája!
Mi köze hozzája,
Hamis a zuzája,
Alázatos szolgáial

El is mennek én magához jómadár'
Ha nem lenne olyan csípi-csapodár!
Mi köze hozzája,
Ha meg nem probálja,
Alázatos szolgája!
Mi köze hozzája,
Ha meg nem probálja,
Alázatos szolgája!

Tizenkettö, tizenhárom, tizenhat
Biz én tölem akár hoppon maradhat!
Mi köze hozzája,
Meghalok utána,
Alázatos szolgája!
Mi köze hozzája,
Meghalok utána,
Alázatos szolgája!

Huszonkettö, huszonhárom, huszonnégy
Adj egy csókot, mézédeset ha elmégy,
Mi köze hozzája,
Várjon a sorjára
Alázatos szolgája!
Mi köze hozzája,
Várjon a sorjára
Alázatos szolgája!

Latzika and Marishka

"Cur - rants hang-ing on the stem, La - tzik - am dear,

Blonde is she who gath - ers them, La - tzik - am dear."

"I'll eat neith - er white nor red, If I did, I'd

lose my head, Ma - rish - kam dear." dear."

"I should like to marry, but, Marishkam dear,
I have neither land nor lot, Marishkam dear."
"Look at me! Within me is
All that you could ever wish, Latzikam dear."

"Yes, but what about the day, Marishkam dear,
When you'll want a fine array, Marishkam dear,
Feathered hat and swirling dress,
Heaven only knows what else, Marishkam dear?"

"God will give us boots and shoes, Latzikam dear,
Everything we need to use, Latzikam dear,
Apricots and corn and pears,
Little pigs with pointed ears, Latzikam dear."

"Well then, turn your pretty head, Marishkam dear,
I will kiss your lips so red, Marishkam dear."
"Promise you will never tell!
Love is heaven and love is hell, Latzikam dear."

Három bokor ribizli, kisangyalom
Szöke kislány szemezi, kisangyalom.
Én biz abból nem eszem
Elmegy tőle az eszem, kisangyalom.

Házasodnám de nekem, kisangyalom
Se földem se egyebem, kisangyalom
Tekintsen rám van nekem
Amit akar mindenem, kisangyalom.

De mi lesz majd, hogyha kö kisangyalom
Fodor csipke karkötö, kisangyalom
Tollas kalap viganó
Meg mi, tudja a manó, kisangyalom.

Ad az Isten bö csizmát, kisangyalom
Pruszlikot meg nagy bundát, kisangyalom
Szölöt búzát barackot
Hegyesfülü malacot, kisangyalom.

Erre forditsd az orcád, kisangyalom
Megcsókolnám pici szád, kisangyalom.
Jaj ne mondja megteszem,
Furcsa az a szerelem, kisangyalom.

Megkivánnám igazán, kisangyalom
A subámba takarnám, kisangyalom
Ne takarjon be nagyon
Úgy is melegem vagyon, kisangyalom.

In My Yard Violets

"In my yard vi - o - lets blos - som now so thick - ly.
Sweet - heart mine, lit - tle dove, come and kiss me quick - ly!"
"No, no, no, no, I am too a - fraid.
Lads are li - ars, al - ways cheat a maid." maid."

"Where's the gift you declared you would surely get me,
If I'd kiss? How you begged, 'Let me, let me, let me!'
One I gave you, two you took from me.
Not a gift, though, did I ever see!
One I gave you, two you took from me.
Not a gift, though, did I ever see!

"Oh, all right, if you like! Come tonight, but mind you!
Don't come in, hide nearby—I'll come out and find you.
Only be as quiet as a mouse!
Make one sound, and I'll not leave the house!
Only be as quiet as a mouse!
Make one sound, and I'll not leave the house!"

Kék virág, ibolya Kinyilott a kertben,
Tubikám, bubikám jer a kebelemre.
Jaj, jaj, jaj, jaj, nem megyek, félek,
Mert hamisak mind a legények.
Jaj, jaj, jaj, jaj, nem megyek, félek,
Mert hamisak mind a legények.

A multkor is azt mondtad, hogy eljösz vasárnap,
Azt hozol, ami kell, hogy ha megcsókollak.
Alig hogy a csókot megkaptad,
A másikat már magad loptad.
Alig hogy a csókot megkaptad,
A másikat már magad loptad.

Este ha eljönnél, szépen megleshetnél,
Lopva a sötétben megölelhetnél.
De a szemed akkor jól nyisd ki,
Halkan, csendben, ne tudja senki!
De a szemed akkor jól hyisd ki,
Halkan, csendben, ne tudja senki!

That's My Girl

That's my girl, what a girl! What a fine complexion!
See her lips, cherry-red! Really she's perfection!
Cherries grow everywhere, red and round and luscious.
Nowhere else lives a girl pretty as my precious!

Ez az én szeretőm, es a pici barna,
Olyan az orcája mint a piros alma.
Pici piros alma terem minden sorban,
De ilyen szép kislány nem minden bokorban.

I've a Purse

If my purse were full of pennies, would my luck be better?
If I had a horse to ride on, could I surely get her?
Though a horse has got no bridle, he can canter fast—hey!
When a fellow's got no money, he will come in last—hey!

Nincsen pénzem, van erszényem, jó bort ihatnám:
Nincsen lovam, van kantárom, lovagolhatnám.
A jó lónak nem kell kantár, még is büszkén jár, hej!
A rózsámnak van babája, mégis máshoz jár.
A jó lónak nem kell kantár, még is büszkén jár, hej!
A rózsámnak van babája, mégis máshoz jár.

The Fisherman

"By the riv – er stands a lit – tle shed.

There I'll live and fish to earn my bread.

Sweet – heart mine, hap – py I'll be,

If you'll come and live there with me." me."

"If I could, how gladly I would go!
Your heart, my heart, match each other so!
Sweetheart mine, you are my lad.
When you leave me, oh, I'll be sad!
Sweetheart mine, you are my lad.
When you leave me, oh, I'll be sad!

"If I could, how gladly I would go!
But my mother—surely she'll say No!
Sweetheart mine, full well you know,
When you leave me, life will be woe!
Sweetheart mine, full well you know,
When you leave me, life will be woe!

"If I could, dear, that is what I'd do!
When my heart no longer beats for you,
Sweetheart mine, all day I'll cry,
Cry all day and pray I may die!
Sweetheart mine, all day I'll cry,
Cry all day and pray I may die!"

Nagy a feje búsuljon a ló.
Egy kislányért búsulni nem jó.
Gombház, hej! Ha leszakad,
Egy helyébe száz is akad.
Gombház, hej! Ha leszakad,
Egy helyébe száz is akad.

Tisza partján van egy kis ház,
Abba leszek én a halász,
Édesem, kedvesem,
Eljösz-e oda te lakni velem?
Edesem, kedvesem,
Eljösz-e oda te lakni velem?

Elmennék, hogyha lehetne,
A szivünk összeillene;
Mert te vagy mindenem,
Éretted lett szomorú keblem.
Mert te vagy mindenem,
Éretted lett szomorú keblem.

Elmennék én, ha lehetne,
Ha az anyám eresztene,
Hisz tudod, édesem
Nélküled rideg az én életem.
Hisz tudod, édesem
Nélküled rideg az én életem.

Én nefelejcset ültettem
Nefelejcs lesz az én nevem,
Csapodár, csapodár,
Csapodár valamennyi szép leány.
Csapodár, csapodár,
Csapodár valamennyi szép leány.

Wine I Drink

dawn comes steal-ing, Love-ly star, dar-ling dove, beau-ty mine! beau-ty mine!

Now I think I'll go and face you,
Lovely star, darling dove, beauty mine!
When I see you, I'll embrace you,
Lovely star, darling dove, beauty mine!
If my kiss of wine shall taste, girl,
Well, why not? I've gold to waste, girl,
Lovely star, darling dove, beauty mine!
If my kiss of wine shall taste, girl,
Well, why not? I've gold to waste, girl,
Lovely star, darling dove, beauty mine!

All the neighbors say I'm ailing,
Lovely star, darling dove, beauty mine!
Like a candle flame that's failing,
Lovely star, darling dove, beauty mine!
In my heart I know it's true, girl,
None can make me well but you, girl,
Lovely star, darling dove, beauty mine!
In my heart I know it's true, girl,
None can make me well but you, girl,
Lovely star, darling dove, beauty mine!

Vőrős bort ittam az este,
Ragyogó csillagom, galambom.
Fehéret iszom reggelre,
Ragyogó csillagom, galambom.
Részegen megyek én haza,
Kijózanodom hajnalra,
Ragyogó csillagom, galambom.
Részegen megyek én haza,
Kijózanodom hajnalra,
Ragyogó csillagom, galambom.

Akkor aztán hozzád megyek
Ragyogó csillagom, galambom.
Hogy téged átöleljelek,
Ragyogó csillagom, galambom.
Borizü lesz majd a csókom
Node hiszen van benn' módom
Ragyogó csillagom, galambom.
Borizü lesz majd a csókom
Node hiszen van benn' módom
Ragyogó csillagom, galambom.

Azt mondják, hogy beteg vagyok,
Ragyogó csillagom, galambom.
Mint az égő gyertya fogyok.
Ragyogó csillagom, galambom.
Beteg az én szivem tája,
Te vagy annak patikája,
Ragyogó csillagom, galambom.
Beteg az én szivem tája,
Te vagy annak patikája,
Ragyogó csillagom, galambom.

I Have Torn My Sunday Jacket

I have torn my Sun-day jack-et, Pick-ing ber-ries, one, two and three! So my heart will break to piec-es, If you will not come now to me! So my heart will break to piec-es, If you will not come now to me!

Boots you bought me, spurs all golden,
How they jingle, oh, how they creak!
"You are wrong, she never loved you!"
That's their jingle, that's what they speak.
"You are wrong, she never loved you!"
That's their jingle, that's what they speak.

Through the meadow jackdaws flying—
Life deserts me, fades now space.
On my forehead dewdrops falling—
Kisses never fall on my face,
On my forehead dewdrops falling—
Kisses never fall on my face.

Epret szedtem az erdöben,
Mind széttépte a ruhám;
Szét lesz tépve bús szivem is,
Hogyha nem jársz énhozzám.
Szét lesz tépve bús szivem is,
Hogyha nem jársz énhozzám.

Haris szállong künn a réten
Hervadok én réges régen
Hull a permeteg arcomra
Hej, de nem hull a csók rája.
Hull a permeteg arcomra
Hej, de nem hull a csók rája.

The Hussar

"Now I know Oc - tob - er first will be my march-ing day, dear.

Then, no mat - ter how you weep, you'll find I can - not stay, dear.

No - thing you can mend, girl! Why should I pre - tend, girl?

Love can nev - er last for - ev - er, al - ways has to end, girl."

"So, you've told me now what day will be your marching-day, dear.
Do you really think I'll weep because you cannot stay, dear?
Why should I pretend, boy?
I've another friend, boy.
Love can never last forever, love must always end, boy."

Októbernek elsejével, el kell masirozni
Akkor fogsz te kis angyalom keservesen sirni;
Semmi babám semmi
Igy kell annak lenni
Mindenféle szerelemnek vége szokott lenni.

Love's My Permit

Speaks the gallant Captain, "What ho!
Who are you, and where would you go?"
"Do not ask me, Captain, do not ask me, Captain.
I must go wherever he goes!"
"Do not ask me, Captain, do not ask me, Captain.
I must go wherever he goes!"

"Where's your permit? Show it to me!
Hurry up, girl! Come, let me see!"
"I've no permit, Captain. Please don't ask me, Captain.
I must go wherever he goes!
"I've no permit, Captain. Please don't ask me, Captain.
I must go wherever he goes!

"Though I have no permit to show,
I implore you, do not say No!
Love's my permit, Captain, love's my permit, Captain.
I must go wherever he goes!
"Love's my permit, Captain, love's my permit, Captain.
I must go wherever he goes!

"I implore you, do not say No!
As a sutler, please let me go!
If I can't, I'll die, sir! Won't you let me try, sir?
I must serve my country, I too!
"If I can't, I'll die, sir! Won't you let me try, sir?
I must serve my country, I too!"

Seprik a pápai utcát,
Masiroznak a katonák.
Tizenhat esztendös barna kislány
Megyen a regiment után.
Tizenhat esztendős barna kislány
Megyen a regiment után.

Kérdi töle a kapitány:
Hová mégy te barna kislány?
Ne kérdezze tölem, fökapitany,
Megyek a szeretöm után.
Ne kérdezze tölem, fökapitany,
Megyek a szeretöm után.

Állj meg, állj meg, hol a levél?
Hadd tudjam meg, honnan jöttél?
Mit kérdi azt tölem a kapitány?
Megyek a szeretöm után.
Mit kérdi azt tölem a kapitány?
Megyek a szeretöm után.

Kérem kapitány uramat
Ne kérje igazságomat.
Igazságom nekem a szerelem,
A szeretömet keresem.
Igazságom nekem a szerelem,
A szeretömet keresem.

Inkább a kapitányt kérem,
Szánja meg esedezésem,
Vegyen be engem markotányosnak
Hadd szolgáljak a hazának.
Vegyen be engem markotányosnak
Hadd szolgáljak a hazának.

Cherry Gathering

Where have you been living, where have you been living,
That you gather that way?
What a funny village, what a funny village,
Where they gather that way!
There in your village, are you all so witty?
Now we've got to know you, come, and we will show you.
You'll learn fast, my pretty.

Már minálunk babám, már minálunk babám
Az jött a szokásba,
Nem szedik a meggyet, nem szedik a meggyet
Fedeles kosárba;
Felmegy a legény, a meggyfa tetejére,
Lerázza a meggyet, te meg babám szedjed a
Rózsás kötényedbe.

The Draftee

let me kiss you. Ne - ver I'll for - get you, girl!

Three years, sweetheart! Will you wait them,
Pretty rosebud, pigeon mine?
Three long years from next October,
Pretty rosebud, pigeon mine!
Then we'll have a splendid wedding,
Wine in streams and music all night long.
Let me kiss you, let me kiss you.
Never I'll forget you, girl!

Azért hogy én huszár vagyok
Kincsem rózsám galambom,
Októberben abfürolok
Kincsem rózsám galambom;
Sárgaréz sarkantyus csizmám
Huszárosan összepengetem,
De sokszor megöleltelek
Soha el nem feledlek.

Gipsy Tinker

Once we dealt in thread and brushes,
Made fine sieves and brooms of rushes. No good!
Ah, those days! We lived in clover.
Now we eat what pigs leave over, No good!

May the Lord destroy this village!
May He make their pigs all perish! No good!
One fine feast of fine roast ham, it
Wouldn't hurt us any, damn it! No good!

Egész falut összejártam,
Mégis semmit sem kaphattam, jaj, jaj.
Eddig az üstfoldozásból,
És más apró kopácslásból, jaj, jaj.

Tütés madzagot árultunk,
Rostát, ecsetet csináltunk, jaj, jaj,
De már most nincs reménységünk,
Majd malotára szorulunk, jaj, jaj.

Pedig attól úgy irtózunk,
Mint a purdé a puskától, jaj, jaj,
Pedig attól úgy irtózunk,
Mint a purdé a puskától, jaj, jaj.

Forget the World

Grief, I want to drown it, to drown it, I drown it in my gob - let, my gob - let. More wine here! Let me drink it and drink it, For - get the world, for - get it, for - get it!

Love—I want to drown it, to drown it.
I drown it in my goblet, my goblet.
More wine here! Let me drink it and drink it,
Forget my love, deceitful, deceitful!

Fére tölem bubánat, bubánat
Kancsót hajtok utánad, utánad,
Szélös világ csufjára, csufjára
Mögfujtlak egy pohárba, pohárba.

Szilvás Village

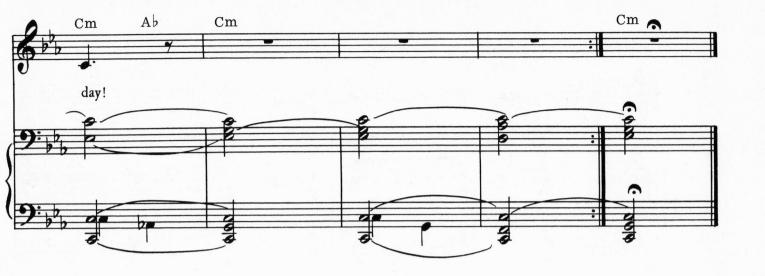

day!

Spoke to him his mother good:
"Come home, Bandi, eat some food!"
"I'll not eat today, Mother,
I'll not eat today, Mother,
This day I will bathe in blood!

"Mother, to the inn I'll go—
There's a brawl to come, I know.
Three of them are soon angry,
Three of them are soon angry,
But the fourth is cold and slow."

Szilvás village mourns today.
Dead the shepherd, once so gay!
Bandi in the grave lying,
Bandi in the grave lying,
Weep, old mother, weep and pray!

Szilvás falu gyászban van,
Juhász legény halva van.
Még szombaton délután
Vigan ment a juh után,
Vigan ment a juh után.

Utána megy az anyja
Gyere haza Bandika!
Nem megyek én ma haza,
Vérben fürdök én még ma,
Vérben fürdök én még ma!

A kocsmába kell menni,
Verekedés fog lenni.
Három juhász inditja,
A negyedik csititja,
A negyedik csititja.

Szilvás falu gyászban van.
Juhász legény halva van.
Sirass anyám, sirass már,
Sirom szélén vagyok már,
Sirom szélén vagyok már.

Woe, Woe, Mother Mine

Sej, haj, édesanyám, huszár a szeretöm,
Elvitte a zsebében a kendöm.
Csak a nevëm rá ne volna irva,
Sej, haj, hogy a szivem ne sajogna érte.
Csak a nevëm rá ne volna irva,
Sej, haj, hogy a szivem ne sajogna érte.

South Slavic

AFTER THE First World War, one of the acts of the Peace Conference was to create a number of new European nations along ethnic lines. The Kingdom of the Serbs, Croats, and Slovenes, usually called Yugoslavia, was one of these. It was composed principally of the districts of Bosnia, Herzegovina, Croatia, Slavania and Bacskz-Barnst to the north, Montenegro, part of Macedonia and Dalmatia to the south, Serbia to the east, South Styria and Carniola to the west. For centuries this group of South Slavic peoples had been thwarted in their natural desire for unity, and had been played off one against the other by the chief European powers.

The complex political history of the Balkan peninsula, lurid and melodramatic as any operetta of "Ruritania," extends almost as far back in time as historical record. The terrain of the peninsula is so mountainous that this district of less than 100,000 square miles was broken up naturally into half a dozen or more small regions, none of them strong enough or self-sufficient enough to develop any independence for long. They were constant prey of their neighbors. Thus, from the eighth to the twelfth centuries, the Serbs were now under Greek, now under Bulgarian control. A brief period of unity under a series of strong leaders made Serbia a kingdom from about 1200 to 1389;

and during the reign of Stephen Dushan, large parts of Greece were annexed. But in 1389 the Turks overran the peninsula, and the disastrous battle of Kossovo spelt the end of independence for both Serbia and Bulgaria. In the next century Turkey completed her conquest of the Balkan countries by invading both Bosnia and Herzegovina. It was not until the nineteenth century that the power of the Asiatic conqueror was threatened, and not until the weird Balkan Wars of 1912-13 that the Turkish yoke was actually removed.

The Turks isolated the South Slavs from Europe even more completely than did the natural barriers of mountain, river and marsh. And by denying education to most of the Slavs, they used ignorance as a further weapon of conquest. But mysteriously throughout the centuries of oppression, the Southern Slavs were silently united. For the folksongs of the peasants kept the Slavic spirit alive. The battle of Kossovo was a Thermopylæ, its memory a badge of disgrace; but the songs incorporating fact and legend concerning the battle were rallying cries to the Serbs, and according to historians were an important force in preserving the identity of the crushed peoples.

The Serbs had their heroes, too; Marko Kraljević (or Marko the King's Son) was the fierce, bold warrior whose exploits inspired many heroic chants. He was a historical figure of the fourteenth century who actually propitiated the Turks; but the folk mind made him a national champion, and endowed him with the superhuman prowess ordinarily associated with the folk hero. Some two hundred epic songs about Marko are extant. He and his fabled steed Sharatz were always a match for their enemies. Alone Marko had the prodigious strength of a Paul Bunyan. Once while he was plowing he was set upon by his enemies; but with his mighty arms he whirled plow and oxen around his head and demolished the at-

tackers. He constantly defied the Sultan, and his sheer bravado and impudence must have delighted the Serbian mind. Marko assumed the character of a Robin Hood, kind to the poor, but spiteful, even cruel toward the rich. His legendary deeds of charity were paralleled in fact by the constant guerrilla warfare of the *haiduks,* or outlaws, who came down from the hillsides (shepherds were often *haiduks,* and vice versa) to harry the Turks by seizing shipments of gold or commodities, which they would divide among their friends. Mountaineer Chetniks of modern Yugoslavia have harried the Nazis with this same bold fearlessness. Heroic songs grew up about these daring raids—most of them tragic, for the *haiduk* was sure to be caught eventually, and to die a dignified, defiant death was the dream of every brave outlaw.

It was such heroic folk songs as those of Kosovo, of Marko Kraljević, and of the Turkish oppression that led the famous Jacob Grimm to remark over a century ago that the ballads of Serbia would, if well known, astonish Europe. "In them," he said, "breathes a clear and inborn poetry such as can scarcely be found among any other modern people." Grimm and Goethe and Walter Scott and the Russian poet Pushkin were excited by these strange new riches, and proceeded to make them known to the world. Grimm saw in the heroic ballads a proof of the debated (and now discountenanced) ballad theory of the epic; the others were content to translate the unsurpassed epic poetry.

The credit for introducing Serbian balladry to the Western world falls to an extraordinary man named Vuk Stefanović Karadzhić (1787-1846). In his youth he began to write down songs he had heard, and an accident that left him a cripple determined the course of the rest of his life. In 1814 he published the first of many volumes of Serbian folk songs. Through his interest in folklore he became friendly with Grimm and Goethe, who were impressed not only by his collections, but also by his scholarly abilities. Karadzhić initiated reforms in the Cyrillic alphabet whereby Serbian became the only European language to possess a completely phonetic alphabet. He compiled a notable dictionary and collected the proverbs of his country. All in all, this little man who eccentrically wore a red fez, even to the grave, was one of the most notable European folklorists of his time.

We have spoken thus far of the heroic ballad, which was sung or chanted to the accompaniment of the *gusla,* the lute-like instrument of one or two strings. The wandering *guslari* preserved the role of the medieval minstrel. They were not only men of capacious memories; they extemporized, they sang primarily for their audience, they cared less for music than for words. Their musical variants were so complex that accurate transcription is almost impossible; moreover, the music is, unfortunately, not significant enough to warrant the inclusion of heroic ballads in the present volume.

Clearly differentiated from the heroic ballads are the so-called women's songs. The latter are largely lyrical and reflective, although narrative songs are not excluded. They are sung by women, girls and young men, chiefly for private amusement. The music is of primary importance; the themes are those common to the domestic folk songs of most other European countries. Incidents of family life, songs of love or hate, songs inspired by work—these topics are universal. If there is anything exceptional in the subject-matter of Yugoslavian women's songs, it is, as Dragutin Subotić has remarked, the close relationship to the life of the people. "Whether people are gathered together at a church festival, or men enjoy their food and drink; whether boys and girls are engaged in gathering corn, or women are spinning around the open fireplaces; whether mothers are journeying to the graves of their children, or youths are dancing a *kolo* on the village green; whether a girl is talking to a nightingale, or a lonely traveller is passing through a forest, these songs accompany every action and event of the people, and it is rightly said that a Yugoslav lives his poetry." [1]

Musically the South Slavic regions vary considerably, despite the relative homogeneity of their language. As one proceeds from north to south he discovers the strong Austrian and German influences in Slovenia giving way to marked Oriental characteristics the further south and east he proceeds. Thus we notice the so-called Gypsy scale (actually of Oriental origin) at the outset of "Coin I Need"; and the same augmented-fourth degree of the scale is to be found in the other songs from regions of Yugoslavia. Another noticeable peculiarity is the fondness for concluding, not on the keynote, but on the supertonic—the second degree of the scale. This fact may ultimately reflect a connection between folk music and ecclesiastical modal tunes, but these are "circular" melodies, sung over and over to a strophic poem, or played repeatedly for dancing; hence there is no need for a decisive final cadence. Still a further characteristic of Yugoslavian folk music is the fondness for duple time. Any appearance of triple time is usually a sign of recent Western corruption.

Like the Czardas in Hungary, the *kolo* is the national dance among the South Slavs. It is, like the *hora* of Rumania, a round dance to the accompaniment of musicians seated in the center of the circle. The music was provided usually by a simple pipe, a drum, and almost always a bagpipe.

---

[1] Dragutin Subotic, *Yugoslav Popular Ballads* (Cambridge, 1932), p. 7.

"Kolo" is a song from the Bosnian district of Yugoslavia. As the words imply, this dancing song is lively and full of gestures which culminate in kissing one's partner. Despite the minor tonality the music is as gay as are the words.

"Coin I Need," also from Bosnia, is an example of the large number of Yugoslavian "women's songs" used only on special occasions. This is a wedding chant, distinctively Eastern in its melancholy. The remoteness suggested by its peculiar scale becomes haunting, once one has become familiar with it.

"Sunce žarko," "Rises the Sun," is one of the most famous of all Slavic melodies—at least to Western ears. For it was used by Tschaikowsky as the theme of *Marche Slav,* that notorious piece of bombast in which the simple Serbian melody is treated as if it were originally heroic and pretentious. César Cui's "Orientale," which begins as a free adaptation of the melody, is more successful in catching the spirit of the lover's lament. In the song, the phrase "From Mitroff's day until St. Peter's" is a formula like "June to January," used here as a symbol of a season of unrest which to a lover must seem like an eternity. "Mitroff's day" is October 26, sacred to St. Demetrius in the Greek Church; St. Peter's day is June 29.

Heinrich Möller in *Das Lied Der Völker* points out the mixture of Oriental and Western elements in "Mercy, Beauty." The first section in recitative is not unlike the Ukrainian *dumka.* The second part, more lively and rhythmical, suggests the atmosphere of central European dancing songs. The poetic theme is, of course, as universal as love itself.

"Lullaby" is a delicately imaginative Montenegrin lullaby with a repetitive melody of small compass. Here the naïve spirit of the folk imagination makes the supernatural seem familiar; not only is the fairy real, but she puts a specific price on the dreams which the mother wishes to buy for her young son Yovan. South Slavic folksong makes much of the supernatural protective spirits, who usually appear more mysterious than the dream-fairy of the present song.

The Bulgarian folk tradition differs from that of the other South Slavs only in details. The most conspicuous fact about the Balkan peninsula is the five-hundred-year occupation by Turkey; it has left its mark on Bulgaria as it has on the Slavs further west. The same fund of heroic and domestic folksong is to be found among all the South Slavs—thus the ballads of Marko Kraljević are sung in Bulgaria, and Marko is a Bulgarian national hero, though he very clearly originated in Serbia. Ballads of the outlaws — *haiduks* (Slavic) or *klephts* (Greek)—also abound, the tragic tone frequently giving way to sheer horror. "The modern Bulgarian ballad-monger," says Entwistle, "is wont not merely to kill, but to butcher." The Asiatic influence on music is strong. Djoudjeff points out the fondness for 5/8 and 7/8 time common to Persian and southeastern Slavic popular music. And he speaks of having heard songs whose words were in both Bulgarian and Turkish—sung now in one language, now in the other. He has even encountered, he says, songs in which the verse is in one language and the refrain in the other. Also peculiar is the Bulgarian fondness for two-beat measures: even complex 5/8, 7/16, 9/16 measures are scrupulously divided into two parts. And finally, Bulgarian poetry, which occasionally uses the Serbian decasyllabic meter, usually prefers the shorter 8- and 6-syllable Rumanian line—but always unrhymed. The English versions of the three Bulgarian songs which follow are of varying meters, but the rhymeless quality is retained in the translations.

"Yelenka" is a dancing song, called *horo* in Bulgaria, and related to the Rumanian *hora,* the Greek *choros,* the Serbian *kolo.* The strongly rhythmic music provides the background for the same kind of round dance commonly found in the other Balkan countries. The theme of the poetry recalls the "hard-hearted Barbara Allen" of British fame. In both songs the high-spirited girl scorns her lover even when she knows he is dying.

"Yanko" is a brief, almost fragmentary *haiduk* ballad. Yanko the outlaw murders a Turk and is himself captured and brought swiftly to justice. Here is little of the bravado of the Serbian *haiduk* pieces; instead one feels the Bulgar's hopelessness in resisting the Asiatic conqueror.

The mother-in-law is an international folk symbol of cruelty. In *"Ganka"* this horrid role is assumed by a young man's sister who is tending his child. Her wrath is being stored not for her brother, it would seem, but for her sister-in-law. In the lyric she does not actually harm the baby, but we can see that her curse would, if the song developed further, lead to some sort of violence, for she is being unnaturally prevented from seeing her sweetheart.

"The Ferryman of Lake Okhrida" is the song of a boatman on the large lake bordering Albania and Yugoslavia, in the old district of Monastir. The song may be considered Macedonian, but it is from a district in which Slavic is spoken, and thus belongs among the present group. The feminine custom of veiling the face (Stanza 2) is an evidence of Turkish influence which spread even beyond the Mohammedans to include many Christian women in European Turkey. The complex time (which is actually 9/8 divided into four instead of the usual three parts) is another sign of Oriental influence.

Kolo

It's a nodding dance we're dancing, a ha ha,
Nodding, nodding, heh heh heh,
Nodding, nodding, heigh heigh heigh!
It's a kissing dance we're dancing, a ha ha,
Kissing, kissing, heh heh heh,
Kissing, kissing, heigh heigh heigh!
Here's the parson come to meddle!
Hold your tongue, don't try to stop us!
Hold your tongue, don't try to stop us!
Heigh heigh heigh!
Here's the parson come to meddle!
Hold your tongue, don't try to stop us!
Hold your tongue, don't try to stop us!
Heigh heigh heigh!

Poigrajmo ovu igru, a ha ha!
Ovu igru, he he he!
Ovu igru, haj, haj, haj!
Poigrajmo ovu igru, a ha ha!
Ovu igru, he he he!
Ovu igru, haj, haj, haj!
Hajd otalen, bundžul pope,
Što zametnu vaku igru,
Što zametnu vaku igru,
Haj, haj, haj!
Hajd otalen, bundžul pope,
Što zametnu vaku igru,
Što zametnu vaku igru,
Haj, haj, haj!

Ovu igru poskakušu, a ha ha!
Poskakušu, he he he!
Poskakušu, haj, haj, haj!
Ovu igru poskakušu, a ha ha!
Poskakušu, he he he!
Poskakušu, haj, haj, haj!
Hajd otalen, bundžul pope,
Što zametnu vaku igru,
Što zametnu vaku igru,
Haj, haj, haj!
Hajd otalen, bundžul pope,
Što zametnu vaku igru,
Što zametnu vaku igru,
Haj, haj, haj!

Coin I Need

"Coin I need to-day, wife, not to-mor-row.
If you have-n't got it, wife, go bor-row!
Take some sacks of grain to town, Make the brok-er pay cash down,
Get our daugh-ter clothes go, end her sor-row!"

"Every girl has shoes to wear but you, girl.
Some girls have both shoes and slippers too, girl.
Every girl has shoes to wear but you, girl.
Some girls have both shoes and slippers too, girl.
Tell me, darling, by the way,
What will your old father say,
When he learns what's up between us two, girl?
Tell me, darling, by the way,
What will your old father say,
When he learns what's up between us two, girl?"

"Well, I think I'll shine my shoes today, boys.
How my sweetheart grieves when I'm away, boys!
Well, I think I'll shine my shoes today, boys.
How my sweetheart grieves when I'm away, boys!
Music now I want to hear.
Play away and never fear—
When I want to have a thing, I pay, boys!
Music now I want to hear.
Play away and never fear—
When I want to have a thing, I pay, boys!"

Ženo moja tri forinta daj mi!
Ako nemaš idi pa uzajmi!
Ženo moja tri forinta daj mi!
Ako nemaš idi pa uzajmi!
Skidaj žito stavana,
Pa kod starog Avrama
Ti pazari, što ti čerka mari!
Skidaj žito stavana,
Pa kod starog Avrama
Ti pazari, što ti čerka mari!

Mercy, Beauty

Mercy, beauty, mercy, hear me!
Mercy, mercy, hear me!
For your neck so white—oh,
I can't sleep at night—oh!
Turn, mill, turn, and grind my grain.
For your neck so white—oh,
I can't sleep at night—oh!
Turn, mill, turn, and grind my grain.

Mercy, beauty, mercy, hear me!
Mercy, mercy, hear me!
When I see your eyes—oh,
Heart within me dies—oh!
Turn, mill, turn, and grind my grain.
When I see your eyes—oh,
Heart within me dies—oh!
Turn, mill, turn, and grind my grain.

Mercy, beauty, mercy, hear me!
Mercy, mercy, hear me!
Mercy, beauty, mercy, hear me!
Mercy, mercy, hear me!

Aman, djevojko,
Uzun ljepoto!
Tvoje ruse kose,
Moju pamet nose,
Samelji mi žito to!
Tvoje ruse kose,
Moju pamet nose,
Samelji mi žito to!

Aman, djevojko,
Uzun ljepoto!
Za te čarne oči
Srce da iskoči,
Samelji mi žito to!
Za te čarne oči
Srce da iskoči,
Samelji mi žito to!

Aman, djevojko,
Uzun ljepoto!
Tvoje grlo bijelo
pamet mi odnelo,
Samelji mi žito to!
Tvoje grlo bijelo
pamet mi odnelo,
Samelji mi žito to!

Rises the Sun

Unfaithful one! Forgotten is the faith you promised?
This you promised when we stood beneath the village maple:

"None else but you! For you I wish to die, beloved."
Where today is what you promised? All your oaths are broken.

From Mitroff's day until St. Peter's may you languish,
Find no peace in soul or body, till my arms embrace you!

Sunce jarko, ne sijaš jednako,
Moj dragane, ne ljubiš jednako,
Il jednako, il nemoj nikako!
Znaš nevero, kako si se kleo,
Na sred sela kod bresta zelena:
Drugu neçu, za tobom umreçu!

A danas si veru prevrnuo,
Bolesna te prevrtala majka,
Od Mitrova do Djurdjeva dana,
Pa ti crna duše ne izašla,
Dok na mome krilu ne zaspao,
Ne zaspao, jade pokajao!

Lullaby

Fay of dreams, can I buy, buy some dreams? What their price?
"All my dreams, all my dreams, ducats four, ducats four!"
I will buy, buy them all, in his bed pour them all.
Like a lamb, like a lamb, Yovan, sleep, sleep and dream!

Luljala, luljala majka sina-na:
Nina-syna, san te prevario,
Prije tebe, nego baba tvoga.
Odtud ide sanovita baka,
Ona voza tvoja kola sanka.

Pošto, bako, tvoja kola sanka?
Ova sanka četiri dukata.
Kupuje jih Jovanova majka,
Pa ih tura Jovu u bešiku;
Zaspa' Jovo kao jagnje ludo.

Yelenka

"Ye - len - ka, Ye - len - ka, sick your love is ly - ing."

"Let him lie, let him lie I am bu - sy danc - ing!

No, no! Here's the place to find my - self a - no - ther.

Go a way, here I stay, now the dance is gay — est!"

"Yelenka, Yelenka, your true-love is dying."
"Yelenka, Yelenka, your true-love is dying."
"Let him die, let him die—I am busy dancing!
Let him die, let him die—I am busy dancing!
No, no! Here's the place to find myself another.
No, no! Here's the place to find myself another.
Go away, here I stay, now the dance is gayest!
Go away, here I stay, now the dance is gayest!"

Elenke, Elenke, momko ti e bolen.
Elenke, Elenke, momko ti e bolen.
Gorko mu, došlo mu, neka bolen leži,
Gorko mu, došlo mu, neka bolen leži.
Khoro neostavjam, momko da si gledam,
Khoro neostavjam, momko da si gledam,
Sega e khroto, tamam naj-dobroto,
Sega e khroto, tamam naj-dobroto.

Elenke, Elenke, momko ti umira.
Elenke, Elenke, momko ti umira.
Gorko mu, došlo mu, neka da umira,
Gorko mu, došlo mu, neka da umira.
Khoro neostavjam, momko da si gledam,
Khoro neostavjam, momko da si gledam,
Sega e khroto, tamam naj-dobroto,
Sega e khroto, tamam naj-dobroto.

Ganka

"May the day come soon now,
O my brother's boy-child,
When one day I rock you, baby,
But the next may mourn you!
When one day I rock you, baby,
But the next may mourn you!

"Would you know my reason,
O my brother's boy-child?
Now I never go for water,
Never meet my sweetheart.
Now I never go for water,
Never meet my sweetheart."

Zaljalaj Ganka,
Bulino detence.
Khem go e ljuljala,
Khem go ljuto klela,
Khem go e ljuljala,
Khem go ljuto klela.

Dano dade Gospod,
Bulino detence,
Dnes da te ljuleja,
Utre da žaleja,
Dnes da te ljuleja,
Utre da žaleja.

Če ot teb ne moga,
Bulino detence,
Za voda da ida,
S libe da se vidja,
Za voda da ida,
S libe da se vidja.

The Ferryman of Lake Okhrida

When you sing, girl, all the lake is shaken,
Like a feather which the wind has taken.
From my heart I pray you, grant me grace, fair one,
Do not lift the veil from your face, fair one.

Raise them not, girl, those fair lids that cover
Eyes so blue! No, burn me not, your lover!
Since another's bride you must be, fair one,
What is left but death now for me, fair one?

Oj djevojče, tenko ta visoko,
Imaš oči jezero globoko.
Koga zborviš čereški mi zrjejet,
Bjeli zobki biserni zagrjejet.

Yanko

War-flag there hoisted, found a Turkish soldier,
Found a Turkish soldier, with his knife killed him.

With his knife killed him, sought a place to hide him,
Found a cold wine-cellar 'neath the green garden.

Thrice before cock-crow Yanko heard the summons.
They have come and taken Yanko to judgment.

Snošti je Janka vev selo vljezla,
Snošti je Janka vev selo vljezla,
Vev selo vljezla bajrak zabila,
Vev selo vljezla bajrak zabila.

Snošti je Janka od Balkan slegla,
Snošti je Janka od Balkan slegla,
Od Balkan slegla, uf selo vlegla,
Od Balkan slegla, uf selo vlegla.

Uf selo vlegla, barjak razvila,
Uf selo vlegla, barjak razvila,
Barjak razvila, puška frlila,
Barjak razvila, puška frlila.

Barjak razvila, puška frlila,
Barjak razvila, puška frlila,
Puška frlila, turčin udrila,
Puška frlila, turčin udrila.

Rumanian

LYING ATHWART the broad lower reaches of the Danube River is the Kingdom of Rumania. The history of the land which before the Second World War answered to this name is so complex that one is surprised at the homogeneity of her peoples. The land was fought over in the days of Trajan and Attila. It lay along the route of the Asiatic conquerors who swarmed across eastern Europe in the early centuries of the Christian era. According to legend, its original settlers were Latins who preserved their allegiance to Rome as jealously as their homesickness allowed them to. Certainly the present language derives from that original settlement. But later claims upon this rich undeveloped territory were made by Slav and Turk. Parts of the land were often in Russia's possession. Turkey had absolute con-

trol of most of it for centuries. The influence also of Greece and Hungary extended within her borders. So that the modern language of the Rumanians, mirroring a kaleidoscopic history, is Latin at the heart, but its polyglot character, part Oriental, part Slavic, is an indelible example of the imprint of the conqueror.

Yet despite the recent unification of the Rumanian peoples—threatened twice already during the twentieth century—this land has maintained a fierce identity, amidst the weight and pressure of foreign influence. Though a rich land, she was not accessible, and exploitation was difficult. To this day, for example, there is only one bridge across the lower eight hundred miles of the Danube. A backbone of the Carpathian Mountains warps across the center of the Kingdom, forming a natural barrier to trade routes. Railroads penetrated the country slowly, and no large concentration of population developed.

With the coming of the twentieth century changes have been rapid. But in this country where farming and grazing were the chief occupations and the inhabitants were characteristically rural, folk art was yet uninhibited when the nineteenth century collectors began to transcribe its songs, and even when not many years ago the famous folklorist Béla Bartók made excursions into various outlying districts, then Hungarian, recording more than 3500 songs and tunes.

In Rumania there is no conscious separation of lyric and narrative songs, as there is in Yugoslavia and to some extent in Bulgaria. But lyric songs dominate. The Rumanian, like the other eastern Europeans, recognize some songs as belonging especially to certain occasions. The *colinde,* for example, are Christmas songs, sung by processions of young people who go through the villages on Christmas eve. There are songs of sadness and death, sung by young and old, but usually chanted or wailed by professional mourners during the burial. There are songs, too, for weddings and harvests.

Even more interesting is the *hora* song. The old *hora,* now sung only by elderly people, was of improvisational character—always sung by a single person, and subject to all sorts of individual variations. More common today, especially among the younger generation, are the relatively recent *hora* melodies, to which most lyrical and epic texts are sung, and which are usually accompanied by dancing. The dancers, holding each other by the hand or around the waist, form a ring with the musicians in the center. The *cobza,* a kind of mandolin with a lute-like neck, and the *gusla,* a crude bowed instrument, joined perhaps by a violin, a bass viol, and a native variety of the bagpipe, play the energetic rhythms of the dancing-song; but

no matter how mad the tempo may become, there is always underneath a tinge of sadness. The tune changes effortlessly from major to minor, but even in the rapid and vivacious dance tempo, a minor or modal scale predominates.

There are two chief rhythms in Rumanian folk music. That of the *doina* is slow, improvisational, full of embellishment—the typical subjective, solo vehicle. The other, belonging to the *hora,* is a strict tempo suitable for dancing purposes, and not subject to whimsical additions at the will of the performer. A dance tune frequently opens with a slow meditative section, followed by the onrush, gradual but steady, of the rapid climactic phrases.

"Ardeleana," the Song of the Little Cuckoo, is a dance tune from the Siebenbürgen region of Transylvania. The pronounced rhythm seems to belie the wistfulness characteristically reflected in the "pathetic fallacy" which transfers the emotions of the lover to the beech leaves and the mountain spring.

"We Must Part" and "Cuckoo" are likewise dancing songs (Ardeleana), both of them conspicuously in the minor mode. "We Must Part" slips into a major cadence four measures from the end, but resolves in that tentative way which reveals it as in fact a continuous tune, repeated indefinitely for dancing. In "Cuckoo" the frequent use of chromatic intervals deepens the intensity of the mood, and recalls the Oriental influences present in Rumanian music.

"What a World!" is a song on a favorite subject—satire of the clergy. To the peasant mind, the presence of a prosperous clergy suggested a lack of proper high seriousness among the spiritual leaders. Here the secular vices are not delicately suggested; with the frankness of Chaucer, the song charges the village priest with using the church contributions to indulge his personal pleasures. Here, as in so many folksongs of southern Europe, the "green leaves" formula appears.

"Stancutza" is a Gypsy song of Transylvania, that district in present Rumania which was once possessed by Hungary, and in which the Hungarian Gypsy influence is most strongly felt.

The augmented and diminished intervals make this a typical Gypsy melody, and the *ostinato* of the keynote in the bass throughout the song is noticeable. The atmosphere is as wild as the music, its spirit almost impossible to translate into English verse.

Ardeleana

Hear the fledgling cuckoo calling! la la la la la.
For his grief the leaves are falling, la la la la la.
Hear the fledgling cuckoo crying! la la la la la.
For his pain the brook is sighing, la la la la.

Cântă puiul cucului, la la la la la, in mijlocul codrului, la la la la la,
Cântă puiul cucului, la la la la la, in mijlocul codrului, la la la la la.
Ş'aşa cântă de frumos, la la la la la la, de cad frunzele pe jos, la la la la,
Ş'aşa cântă de frumos, la la la la la la, de cad frunzele pe jos, la la la la.

Ş'aşa cântă de cu jale, la la la la la, de piеă frunza pe cale, la la la la la,
Ş'aşa cântă de cu jale, la la la la la, de piеă frunza pe cale, la la la la la.
Ş'aşa cântă de cu dor, la la la la la la, de plâng apele'n izvor, la la la la,
Ş'aşa cântă de cu dor, la la la la la la, de plâng apele'n izvor, la la la la.

We Must Part

Though our hearts are but one heart, la la la la la la la,

Though we love, dear, we must part, la la la la la. la la.

Yet to part would be a sin, la la la la la,

You're my twin and I'm your twin, la la la la la la la la.

Like in hates and like in loves, la la la la la la la la,
Just as like as cooing doves, la la la la la la la.
Like in that and like in this, la la la la la,
Most alike, dear, when we kiss, la la la la la la la la.

Vai, bădiţă, dragi ne avem, la la la la la la la,
Vai, bădiţă, dragi ne avem, la la la la la la la.
Nē-am lua, nu ne putem, la la la la la,
Nē-am lua, nu ne putem, la la la la la la la la.

Nē-am lăsa, nu ne'ndurăm, la la la la la la la,
Nē-am lăsa, nu ne'ndurăm, la la la la la la la.
Că prea bine sămănăm, la la la la la,
Că prea bine sămănăm, la la la la la la la la.

Şi la ochi şi la sprâncene, la la la la la la la,
Şi la ochi şi la sprâncene, la la la la la la la.
Ca doi porumbei la pene, la la la la la,
Ca doi porumbei la pene, la la la la la la la la.

Şi la stat şi la umblat, la la la la la la la,
Şi la stat şi la umblat, la la la la la la la.
Şi la dulce sărutat, la la la la la,
Şi la dulce sărutat, la la la la la la la la.

Cuckoo

Perch upon a dahlia flower, la la la la la la la la la,
Tell her how I wait each hour, la la la la la la la la la.
Perch upon a spray of clover, la la la la la la la la la,
Tell her, cuckoo, how I love her, la la la la la la la la la.

Cucule cu peană sură, la la la la la la la la la,
Nu-mi cânta pe arătură, la la la la la la la la la;
Ci sa-i cânti mândrii pe sură, la la la la la la la la la,
Sa-mi trimită un pic de gură, la la la la la la la la la.

Pe o floare de bujor, la la la la la la la la la,
Sa nu-i duc atâta dor, la la la la la la la la la;
Pe o floare de gheorghină, la la la la la la la la la,
Să grăbească şi să viňa, la la la la la la la la la.

What a World!

Caught him in my pock-et feel-ing! (What a world! What a world!)

When the springtime brought fair weather, (What a world! What a
    world!)
Three he counted, three together, (What a world! What a world!)
Mountain maiden, valley maiden, (What a world! What a world!)
City maiden, jewel-laden. (What a world! What a world!)

Mountain maiden went to marry, (What a world! What a world!)
Valley maiden would not tarry, (What a world! What a world!)
City maiden got quite fretful, (What a world! What a world!)
City maiden grew forgetful. (What a world! What a world!)

Popa dice că nu bea, lumea mea, lumea mea,
L'am prins la butia mea, lumea mea, lumea mea.
Popa dice că nu fură, lumea mea, lumea mea,
L'am prins la mine'n tesilă, lumea mea, lumea mea.

Foaie verde bob năut, lumea mea, lumea mea,
Trei amante a avut, lumea mea, lumea mea.
Una'n deal şi una'n vale, lumea mea, lumea mea,
Una'n ulita cea mare, lumea mea, lumea mea.

A din deal s'a măritat, lumea mea, lumea mea,
A din vale la lăsat, lumea mea, lumea mea.
A din ulița cea mare, lumea mea, lumea mea,
L'a pus şi ea l-a uitare, lumea mea, lumea mea.

Popa dice că nu bea, lumea mea, lumea mea,
L'am prins la butia mea, lumea mea, lumea mea.
Popa dice că nu fură, lumea mea, lumea mea,
L'am prins la mine'n tesilă, lumea mea, lumea mea.

Stancutza

He who passes, he who sees her, breaks his journey, loves her madly,
Drinks until his purse is empty. Morning finds him thinking sadly.
Ouf, who could ever pass her house and not be taken?
Ouf, who could ever see her face and not be shaken?
Ouf, he who stays there, though he comes with ox and wagon,
Ouf, he is lucky when he leaves with just a rag on!

La bordei cu crucea naltă, la Stăncuţa sprâncenată,
Joacă hora încheiată, curge lumea fermecată.
Of! vinu-i bun, ocana-i mică,
Of! beau voinicii del usucă,

Of! nu se'ndură să se ducă,
Of! noaptea la ea îi apucă.

Cine trece, se opreşte cum o vede 'nebuneşte,
Bea vin, punga-şi cheltueşte, dumineaţa se căeşte.
Of! cine poate ca să treacă,
Of! să o vază, să nu-i placă,
Of! şi conacul stând să-şi facă,
Of! din patru boi cu doi pleacă.

Cine vine de-a călare cheltueşte tot ce are,
Iar de n' are'n buzunare pleacă cu şeaua'n spinare.
Of! iar pe jos oricine vine,
Of! işi bea tot de lângă sine,
Of! du-mi-te, neică, cu bine,
Of! că folos nu am de tine.

Greek

FOLK MUSIC in Greece has a great deal in common with that of the rest of the Balkan peninsula. For like the South Slavs, the Greeks were subjected to centuries of Turkish domination. The history of the whole region, complex though it has been, is a uniformly grim record of half a thousand years of almost complete isolation from the rest of Europe and the slow but steady development of a national feeling which ultimately threw off the Asiatic conqueror. The Kingdom of Greece today is undergoing a period of change and upheaval, and is currently under the rule of the army. By comparison with modern methods of conquest, the Turkish dominion over the Greeks was benevolent; indeed the Byzantine influence in many ways enriched modern Greek civilization.

Two traditions of folk music have been important in recent centuries. One, that of the mountainous rural areas, is represented by the familiar heroic songs of the outlaw. The Slavic *haiduks* were paralleled in Greece by the *klephts* (the word is from the root that gives us the English *kleptomaniac,* and means literally "thief"). These robbers resided chiefly in the rugged western regions of Epirus, and like their Slavic confreres subsisted on sheep from the hillsides and booty from the towns. Their songs, or songs about them, were frequently news letters of their activities. Thus a ballad of famous eighteenth-century klephtic chief Niko Tzaras recounts how in an almost formal battle he exhorted his men to put steel in their hearts and iron on their feet. Then "they forthwith rushed on and reached the bridge [held by the Turks], and Niko Tzaras cut the chain of the bridge with his damask steel and so they gained the other side." [1] The personal side of the klepht's dangerous life is seen when in a ballad the outlaw's wife awakens to find that he has come down from the hills to have his wounds bandaged. She binds him up, but not without giving him a stern lecture on the danger he is running by coming into civilization.

The Greek war of independence early in the last century, made familiar by Lord Byron's dramatic participation, had its heroes who were celebrated in song. One of them was Marco Bozzaris, who led the Greeks in the Missolonghi campaign, and whom a contemporary American poet considered

One of the few, the immortal names,
That were not born to die.

In one of the ballads the Turks try to buy off the Greek defenders, but having learned the meaning of liberty by bitter experience, they give battle. The Turks "fall as thick as frogs" from the Greek muskets and sabers.

The historical and heroic ballads were chanted by professional wandering rhapsodists. They are characteristically primitive in expression, their music of little consequence even to the singer. They are the product of courage, of desperation, of the fierce fight for survival. And, except for recent ballads, they come from a life of solitude and hardship.

The populous coastal towns and the Aegean Islands have given us urban songs of a strikingly different character. From the commercial centers accustomed to trade with other Mediterranean countries comes a softer strain of domestic and romantic songs. They are more melodious than the heroic chants. They are frequently cosmopolitan, tinged with Byzantine

and Italian influences simultaneously. Yet they are clearly Balkan in character. Besides the usual themes of love, hate, superstition, lament, and the like, there is a large body of "occasional" songs such as we have observed in all the Slavic countries—marriage and funeral songs, *kalenda* for the Christmas season, swallow songs for springtime, and, inevitably with such a scattered race as the Greeks were until recently, songs of exile.

The Greeks had their dancing songs, called the *choros,* which by the very etymology of the name shows the Greek ancestry of the Rumanian *hora,* the Serbian *kolo,* the Bulgarian *horo.* They were sung to the accompaniment of complex steps and gestures. As Abbott describes them, "At weddings and festivals men and women dance together in a ring, holding each other's hands. The leader of the dance, as he sweeps on, waves a handkerchief and sings out the verses of the song, while the rest join in the chorus."

"The Curse" was collected by L. A. Bourgault-Ducoudray in Smyrna, Asia Minor. It is a good example of the romantic Greek song with Eastern flavoring. Here the scale is what is sometimes called the Oriental chromatic. Actually, so far as we see it in the limited range of this tune, it is our familiar G minor scale. Yet the song ends, not on the keynote of the scale, but on the dominant. There is nothing regional in the lover's anathema against whoever spread the scandalous rumors which caused his mistress to leave him.

"Mount Agrafa" is a brief love song of central Greece. The foreign quality of the music is here even more obvious than in "The Curse," as the chromatic intervals suggest now one ecclesiastical mode, now another. The primitive character of the song is carefully preserved by Dr. Deutsch's simple accompaniment with its open chords throughout the bass part.

---

[1] George F. Abbott, *Songs of Modern Greece* (Cambridge, 1900), p. 31.

The Curse

Did you not tell me, dearest girl,
That you would die if we should part?

Now you forsake me, now you say,
"I know you not, we never met."

Anathema ton pouvale skanthal'ana
Mesa mas ke then afeenee na perno
'San prota ton keron mas!
Then eesoun see pou me leges
An then se dio petheno?
Ke tora perpatees ke les:
Pou s'eetha? pou se xero?

Mount Agrafa

Up Mount A - gra - fa let me go. I'll sit

down on a stone, think - ing, star - ing be - low.

There I will rest my head, there I'll fall dream - ing,

There I will dream a dream, all of my sweet - heart.

Aneveeka sta Agrafa
K'apano sta katsavraha

Ligon eepno yia na paro
Tin agapee mou yia navro.

American

AMERICA WAS NEVER in greater need of understanding European peoples. The first sixty years of this century have taught us nothing if they have not taught us that we cannot live alone in the world. Neither can we any longer judge other civilizations by the rather special criteria of our own particular tribalism. One step toward the solution of our difficulties may lie in seeing that there are certain common denominators of human nature that link all mankind. The Greek humanists understood this, but in recent centuries national and racial idol-worship has diverted man's eyes from this enduring truth. The five American songs in this book, songs whose beauty is their own truth, show that while every folk has its individuality, its own idioms, there are great themes which the folk of all nations spontaneously develop in song.

America's folk music has variety above all,

and an informality which can be only suggested in our collection. The songs of mining and lumber camps, of cowboys on the range, of the secluded mountain folk and the infectious play party, the ballads of bad men and jealous lovers—these constitute a large body of song sometimes hearty, sometimes sad, but always richly colloquial. The five songs here present seem to combine musical distinction and folk interest in a happy union.

"The Putney Hymn" is an eighteenth-century hymn which has since slipped into the category of a white spiritual. It now circulates orally among folk who have no idea of its origin or authorship. Yet it is not a purely folk product. The words are by Isaac Watts, one of England's most famous hymn writers; the music is by the pioneer American musician William Billings (1746-1800). Billings' books were published in Boston, but after his wild and rather illiterate harmonies had fallen out of popularity in New England, they flourished in the South, and many of his hymns were reprinted in some of the nineteenth-century "buckwheat" hymnals of the fundamentalists. That is probably the beginning of this hymn's history. The fashion of giving place-names to tunes was not original with Billings, although it became a kind of trade-mark with him as he drew his titles from scores of towns and villages with which he was familiar (this tune is named for Putney, Vermont). The *Este Psalter* (1592) is perhaps the earliest English collection with place-name titles, and the practice was introduced into New England early in the eighteenth century.[1]

"Go Ter Sleep" is a cradle-song whose idiom is sharply to be differentiated from European songs of the same sort. Not only is the musical idiom individualized, but the song is

---

[1] See Hamilton C. MacDougall, *Early New England Psalmody* (Brattleboro, 1940), p. 13.

matter-of-fact rather than romantically beautiful.

Elie Siegmeister, in his comment on "O Death!" in *A Treasury of American Song*, says that there are people in the Kentucky mountains who, while they cannot read or write, know their Bible thoroughly and can cite many passages entire, both chapter and verse. In this region the story is told of a preacher who paid no heed to the Lord's call to preach, who was stricken and then laid out for dead. But he rose up, stiff and cold, and asked the Lord to spare him, in the dramatic lines of this song.

"I'm Just A-Goin' Over Jordan" is a Negro version of a white spiritual whose title is "A Poor Wayfaring Stranger." This plaintive melody has given rise to a number of variants, and it is likely that it was first learned by Negroes who used to accompany their white masters to church. In one of its several forms it has been popular among the fundamentalists of the Southeastern states for a century. Music of a strange and powerful quality is a staple of the religious lives of thousands in rural areas, and their periodical "Sacred Harp" singing conventions are widely attended. Their shaped-note hymnals are marvels of intricate and melodious part-writing. "A Poor Wayfaring Stranger" appears in such collections as *The Primitive Baptist Hymn and Tune Book* (1902) and *Good Old Songs* (1913), and was used as a musical signature on broadcasts:

> *I'm just a poor wayfaring stranger,*
> *Trav'ling through this world of woe,*
> *And there's no sickness, no toil and trouble,*
> *In that fair land to which I go.*
> *I'm going there to see my mother,*
> *I'm going there, no more to roam;*
> *I'm just a-going over Jordan,*
> *I'm just a-going over home.*

"Crucifixion" is one of the most eloquent of all the Negro spirituals. This heart-rending version of Christ's death on the cross is as vivid as if the original poet had been an eye-witness. We cannot but be impressed by the remarkable language, simple yet everywhere dignified and effective. The occasions are few when the genius of poetic imagination seizes upon the indubitably right word. Here the use of "mumbalin'" and "twinklin'" is nothing less than inspired, and the repetition of "not a word" adds great forcefulness to the tragic melody.

The Putney Hymn

Go ter Sleep

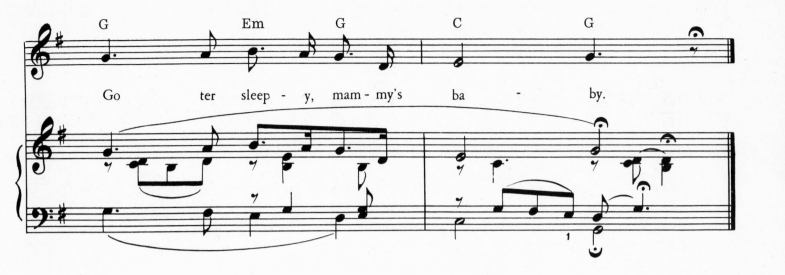

Go ter sleep, go ter sleep,
Go ter sleepy, mammy's baby,
All de horses in de stable
B'longs ter mammy's little baby.

O Death!

I'll lock your jaws till you can't talk,
I'll bind your legs till you can't walk,
I'll close your eyes so you can't see.
I will bring you unto me.
O death! O death!
Can't you spare me over for another year?

Over Jordan

there to meet my fath - er, I know he'll (she)

meet me when I come. I'm just a -

go - in' ov - er Jor - dan, I'm just a -

go - in' ov - er home.

For additional stanzas, replace "father" with "mother", then "brother", then "sister".

Crucifixion

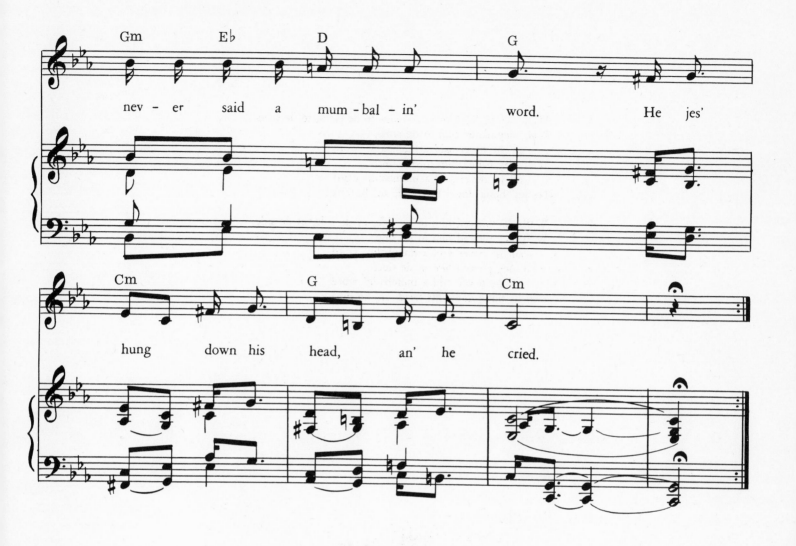

Oh, dey crowned him wid a thorny crown, thorny crown, thorny crown.
Oh, dey crowned him wid a thorny crown,
    an' he never said a mumbalin' word.
Oh, dey crowned him wid a thorny crown,
    an' he never said a mumbalin' word.
He jes' hung down his head, an' he cried.

Well, dey nailed him to de cross, to de cross, to de cross.
Well, dey nailed him to de cross,
    an' he never said a mumbalin' word.
Well, dey nailed him to de cross,
    an' he never said a mumbalin' word.
He jes' hung down his head, an' he cried.

Well, dey pierced him in de side, in de side, in de side.
Well, dey pierced him in de side,
    an' he never said a mumbalin' word.
Well, dey pierced him in de side,
    an' he never said a mumbalin' word.
Den he hung down his head, an' he died.

Well, dey nailed him to de cross, to de cross, to de cross.
Well, dey nailed him to de cross,
    an' he never said a mumbalin' word.
Well, dey nailed him to de cross,
    an' he never said a mumbalin' word.
He jes' hung down his head, an' he cried.

Well, dey pierced him in de side, in de side, in de side.
Well, dey pierced him in de side,
    an' he never said a mumbalin' word.
Well, dey pierced him in de side,
    an' he never said a mumbalin' word.
Den he hung down his head, an' he died.